Birds Of Passage

Birds Of Passage

by

BERNICE RUBENS

HAMISH HAMILTON LONDON

First published in Great Britain in 1981 by
Hamish Hamilton Ltd
Garden House 57–59 Long Acre London WC2E 9JZ

Copyright © 1981 by Bernice Rubens

British Library Cataloguing in Publication Data

Rubens, Bernice
  Birds of passage
  I. Title
  823'.914[F]   PR6068.U2

ISBN 0-241-10664-8

Set by Saildean Limited, Surrey
Printed in Great Britain by
St Edmundsbury Press, Bury St Edmunds, Suffolk

Contents

CHAPTER ONE

A certain lack of synchronisity

Neighbours. That's what they were, Ellen Walsh and Alice Pickering, with a thin wall between their sitting-rooms and an even thinner one between their bedrooms on the first floor. An eavesdropping house of which both the Walshes and the Pickerings took full advantage. And had been so doing for nigh on forty years. It could fairly be said that they knew each other pretty well, in the private as well as the public domain. Sometimes they confused those facts that were officially known with the information they had gleaned from bricks-and-mortar echo. But, since the pursuit of eavesdropping was common to both sides, each overlooked the others' indiscretion. In all respects, they were good neighbours, and what sealed their togetherness was the hedge that joined their two terraced estates. It stretched from the Walsh's front gate to the Pickering's with no outward sign of hesitation at its centre as to a change of ownership. It was straight as a die from one holding to the other. Every Saturday morning, Mr Walsh would stand at his gate, shears at the ready. And Mr Pickering likewise. The two men would nod to each other, and silently shear their way to a central encounter. They worked at the same efficient pace, arriving simultaneously at the half-way point, where they would pause and exchange morning greetings. And when one day, late in the spring, their other neighbours noted that the Walsh hedge was growing untamed, towering over the Pickering holding with a certain helpless impudence, they took it as a sure sign that Mr Walsh was indisposed. But it was more than that, as further enquiries and certain visible evidence proved. Mr Walsh had gone to his Maker, and his holding in the hedge was orphaned.

Now, Mr Pickering had never coveted his neighbour's wife,

even when Mr Walsh was alive and shearing; now that he was dead, he coveted her even less. Even so, to shear his late neighbour's portion would, in his mind, have been tantamount to a delayed and public adultery. So he refrained, much as their common frontage now displeased him. He would have to wait until Mrs Walsh herself invited him to husband her hedge. But Mrs Walsh issued no such invitation. As the hedge grew, shadowing her sitting-room and the mourning within, she harboured a deep resentment of Mr Pickering simply because he was still alive. She didn't care how high her hedge grew, or how untidily. It would be a constant reminder to Pickering that he had outstayed his welcome. Let him depart as her Walsh had done, and let Alice's hedge reach for the skies like her own. For, over a year ago, she and Alice had made plans as to how to disport themselves together once decently widowed. Now, with Pickering's survival, those plans would have to be delayed. Nowadays she could hardly acknowledge him, and the poor and innocent Pickering ascribed her rudeness to her bereavement.

It had been their custom, on New Year's Eve of every year, to celebrate in each other's houses, each taking the rites in turn. In the beginning, when both families were new to the street, their children had gathered together and listened to the bells on the wireless. Later it was television, but, by that time, the children had married and left home. A year ago, the celebrations were conducted in the Walsh house, in the days when the hedge did not trellis the windows and all was reasonably well between the paper-thin walls. They had a roast beef supper, Mrs Walsh's speciality – Mrs Pickering went in for roast lamb. The champagne stood on the sideboard awaiting the midnight bell. At the stroke of twelve, according to the television, Mr Walsh aimed the cork at the floor and filled their glasses. Their eyes watered, a prelude to nostalgia, and the neighbours linked arms, and along with their television hosts, they sang *Auld Lang Syne*. That done, Mr Pickering kissed his spouse, and Mr Walsh likewise. Then the ladies clasped each other tenderly, while the men waited on the side-lines in deference to that law which endorses the male embrace only after a goal scored in a football match. Then Mr Pickering would kiss Mrs Walsh on her cheek, and

2

Mr Walsh would do his New Year's duty by his neighbour's wife. Then together they would reminisce, with laughter, longing and infinite sentimentality. To recall the past, the first meetings, marriage, the birth of children was a reliable defence against the corroding boredom of familiarity. On each New Year's Eve, the recollections of loving, of the youth and beauty of the past, diluted the present reality of the whispering behind walls, the sobbing at bed-time and the morning rage. It would see them through another year. Thus formalities were observed and, after their journeys into the past, the gentlemen would watch television, while the ladies cleared the table.

On their last celebration, Ellen and Alice had not re-joined their spouses. They had remained in the kitchen. Ellen sat at the table and poured the freshly brewed tea. Alice sat beside her. It had seemed quite natural to both women that there was a need to be with each other for a while, a mutual recognition, perhaps, in view of all their talk of the past, that the future was diminishing. Walsh's asthma was worsening and Pickering's ulcers were no better. It did not occur to either woman that their husbands would survive them. It was time to think of their approaching widowhood.

Ellen looked across at her friend. She noticed how Alice was fingering the cloth of her dress, rubbing the material between her fingers, smoothing it onto her flesh. She's getting old, Ellen thought, and then noticed that she was doing exactly the same herself. And Alice looked at her friend and thought that, though they were more or less the same age, Ellen was wearing less well. Alice sipped her tea. 'Ellen,' she said, and she laid her hand on her friend's arm. She picked a tuck of the sleeve and rubbed it between her fingers.

'What is it, Alice?' Ellen said and found her own fingers straying to a pleat on Alice's skirt. To finger one's own clothes is to test one's mortality. To finger the clothes of others is to acknowledge that that mortality is shared. It was a moment of deepest intimacy. It was a moment to suggest a cruise.

Which Alice did. 'When we're both widowed,' she added.

'Oh that will be fun,' Ellen said, then clapped her mouth on the blasphemy lest the fun was heard to refer to her husband's demise. But she had to admit to herself that widowhood would indeed be a diversion; that already, on each successive New Year, it was more difficult to recollect the joys of the past, filtered as they were by the passionless present. Indeed she could hardly remember them at all. Yet they must have been, those glad days, since her Walsh seemed to recall them with ease. Or did he too invoke them only as a principle? She didn't want him to die, but she wanted to survive him. She wanted a little time without him, a chance to come into her own. She would not have been surprised to know that Alice's thoughts dwelt on the same lines.

'We must be decently widowed,' Ellen said, and 'decent' referred to time. Time to let the grass grow, time to dry out the tears, time to exhaust others' sympathy and patience.

Thus they had come to an agreement, and it did not occur to either of them that their achievement of widowhood might not be simultaneous. As it turned out, synchronisity did not oblige. Mr Walsh had departed in the following spring, leaving Ellen widowed and Alice still pinned to her wifehood.

On the following New Year's Eve, Ellen had gone to the Pickerings alone. It was an irritable evening. A quartet is not adaptable to trio-playing any more than *Auld Lang Syne* is orchestrated for one. Mr Pickering was embarrassed, Ellen ashamed, Alice tetchy. Mr Walsh's demise had thrown out the arrangement of her supper-table. For a moment she wished that by next year her friend would have married again, but then quickly withdrew that wish, in fear or hope of her own widowhood, and a further postponement of their cruise.

By the spring of that year Ellen had already served her 'decent' year, while Mr Pickering still flourished. And, moreover, showed no signs of wilting. His hedge-holding, clipped to a leaf's-breadth, was infuriating proof of his stubborn survival, and the foliage that now shrouded her windows served only to darken the already black rage in Ellen's heart.

Each time Alice saw her friend, she felt she had to apologise for her continuing wedlock. Occasionally she offered Ellen a little hope, though her spirit balked at the treachery. 'His ulcers are very bad today,' she would say; and when Ellen did not sufficiently react, she would specify her prognosis: 'I don't know how much longer he can go on,' and, as she said it, she resented Ellen for her unspoken demands on her own disloyalty. Ellen was really a bit of a bully, Alice thought, and Alice would return to her kitchen and seethe. 'It's not my fault she lost her husband,' she would mutter, 'and it's not my fault that I kept mine.' She dreaded their next New Year's gathering.

It was Ellen's turn. The roast beef era had passed, along with its carver. Ellen did a strogonoff from a recipe she'd heard on the wireless. It was foreign and would make an impression not only on her neighbours but on Mr Thomas, a new-comer. The Pickerings were much unnerved by his presence. Especially Alice. Was her friend on the point of marrying again? Thomas was a robust-looking man and, from his large appetite, clearly without ulcers, and threatened yet again the simultaneity of their joint widowhood. The prospect of the cruise was considerably dimmed. That year it was Mr Thomas who popped the champagne as they raised their glasses to the television choir. But they did not sing. Mr Pickering hummed a little for old time's sake, but Thomas was an outsider, who was not allowed to sing their tune. Ellen avoided the kitchen-chat after supper and the evening broke up early. Alice took the unasked question into her own sitting-room.

'Who was that Mr Thomas?' she said. 'I've never seen him before.'

Mr Pickering was unhelpful, and then, as an afterthought, without any notion of its relevance, he said, 'I do wish she'd get that hedge cut.'

For relevant it was, because Mr Thomas had made his first appearance on Mrs Walsh's doorstep with the request that he might clip her hedge. Mrs Walsh was astonished. She felt assaulted, as if the stranger were making a certain suggestion, a proposition perhaps, for which the hedge-clipping was only a cover. Over the years since her husband's demise, the green foliage had seemed to corset her, to strait-jacket her body into a repaired virginity. She had grown intact, as it were. Which was why she was glad Pickering had never touched her hedge. And now this stranger was on her doorstep with his sugges-tion, and, in Ellen's mind, it was a request to bed her. She looked at him hard, and found him not unattractive. She decided the hedge would remain intact. He would have to marry her before he deflowered it.

After that New Year's Eve, the Pickerings were accustomed

to seeing Mr Thomas, who was now a daily gentleman caller. Ellen kept their wedding very quiet, so Mr Pickering was astonished, to say the least, when, one Saturday morning, as was his wont, he took up his hedge-post and saw, through the jungle of foliage, a very positive human shape on the other end. And heard the unmistakable clipping of shears.

Ellen Walsh looked through her net curtains, shuddering with each thrust of the blade, and, like a bride, she thrilled to a second coming. She now belonged to Thomas as legally as she had once belonged to Walsh.

Alice Pickering, whose head had been shamefully bowed since Mr Walsh's passing, now lifted it, and felt a lot less guilty. She no longer apologised for her husband's survival and, when she did refer to his ulcers, it was with confidence and no shame that they were getting better. She rather looked forward to their next New Year's Eve celebration.

But poor Thomas never made it. Robust as he was, and ulcerless, it is possible that he died simply of his rude sound health, too rude, and too sound perhaps, for his own good. Whatever, one Saturday morning, on reaching for his shears, while Ellen waited at the net-curtained window, he collapsed and cheated her. She couldn't understand it. No-one could. It was his heart, the doctor said, but Ellen didn't believe him. There was nothing wrong with Thomas's heart. Some people survived, she decided, with a terrible glance in Pickering's direction, and others simply died. Her Thomas had died of death, and that was all there was to it.

Her neighbours watched the hedge grow once more, and wondered what on earth it was that Ellen Walsh did to her men. Ellen Walsh she still was to them. They hadn't yet grasped the Thomas handle in her connection, and now it was hardly worth their pains. The hedge grew and grew, shrouding Ellen's windows once more. Poor Alice. She could hardly make a public appearance, so ashamed was she of Pickering's survival.

That year, they celebrated New Year's Eve not at all. Ellen went to her daughter up North, and the Pickerings watched television on their own. That year Mr Pickering didn't even hum *Auld Lang Syne*. It never worked without the presence of a third party, single or otherwise. It was silly singing it just to Alice. It would have embarrassed them both.

6

When Ellen came back shortly after the New Year, the hedge had grown with a vengeance, and she was obliged to keep the light on in her living-room during the daylight hours. But not again, she decided. Not another hedge-cutter. She would let it grow, curl around her roof-tops, and shroud her in its evergreen balm. And she would wallow within it, waiting for old Pickering to die.

She had no intention of serving a 'decent' year for Thomas. There was hardly any point in mourning a man for longer than you had known him. As soon as Pickering popped off, she would persuade Alice to curtail her 'decent' year. It was the least Alice could do. Nowadays Ellen could hardly look at Pickering, and Alice had become her apologetic worst. Pickering's ulcers were no better, and she understood less and less, and at each meeting, how he managed to survive at all.

Sometimes Alice looked at her husband and the thought occurred to her that she might not even outlive him, that he and Ellen were the great survivors, and that it would be she who would earn the 'decent' year, and Ellen and Pickering the cruise. Then she began to dislike Ellen and she kept herself indoors for a long time.

It was during this period when Ellen saw little of her friend, that, one Saturday morning, the clipping did not awaken her. She opened her eyes to mid-morning on the clock, and dashed out of bed to the window. The usual flat-sheared edge of the Pickering hedge was rudely unbalanced by a week's growth. No tell-tale clippings lay on the path, and hope surged in Ellen's heart. She put her ear to the common wall between, and the silence from that direction fed her hopes. Illness was never silent. A groan, a whisper or a scream were tokens of pain or indisposition. Even resignation merited a sigh. But that quality of silence from behind the wall, the silence without echo, the silence of footsteps that were never taken, of sighs that stayed in the throat – that silence was reserved for Death alone.

She dressed and knocked on Alice's door. Alice opened it almost immediately, and the two women stared at each other for a long while.

'Yes,' Alice said at last, and Ellen followed her into the house.

They sat at the kitchen table. A lone tear dropped from

Alice's eye. 'I think there's something about that hedge,' she said. 'It's got the devil in it.'

'What happened?' Ellen said, after a pause.

'He collapsed. Just fell down on the hall floor. The shears were in his hand. A heart-attack, the doctor said.'

He died of hedge, Ellen thought, like the rest of them. 'Let's cut it down,' she said suddenly. 'Let's poison the roots of it.'

Alice smiled. She was thinking of the cruise, and she crushed Ellen's apron between her fingers. Ellen did likewise with Alice's shawl. It was a moment of forgiveness, a mutual pardon for the curses that each woman in their time had laid on the other.

'Can I see him?' Ellen said. Alice had offered to see her Walsh, and she felt bound to do the same duty by Pickering.

She followed her up the stairs. Pickering lay in that silence that Ellen had heard through the wall. He looked deeply ashamed and Ellen was suddenly very sorry for him. He was entitled to a 'decent' year, she thought, and as if Alice was reading her, she said, 'We'll take our cruise in the spring.'

They clasped each other and wept together, both for the losses of the past and the possible joys of the future.

After the funeral, an odd-job man came and poisoned the hedge on both sides. Its demise was slow and possibly painful, for it took some months to die, and it was almost spring before it shed its last offended branch. And then, astonished at the sudden light, the daffodils and irises stretched their necks to view the unaccustomed street and the figures of two women of a certain age, arm in arm, suitcases at their feet, waiting for the taxi to pull into the kerb. Between them they added up to the total of one hundred and twenty-six years, though neither would admit to the sum of her own share. One lies about one's age only when one is not proud of it. A litttle girl will boast her calender as proof of her growth; an old woman will trumpet her years in pride of her survival. Ellen Walsh and Alice Pickering dwelt in that no-man's land between, a land that idled between the reachable borders of innocence.

As they settled themselves in the back of the taxi, Alice said, 'Pickering would have loved a cruise.' And Ellen felt obliged to offer a similar token of regret, though she was undecided as to the target. Thomas would have been more fun, but Walsh was more worthy, simply because he had served longer. 'So would Walsh,' she said.

It was a formality, for both women knew that their pursuit was never considered a coupled one. It belonged to widow-hood, a status in which both women, after a series of unfortunate ill-timings, were now amply qualified.

CHAPTER TWO

An ominous pairing

Equally qualified, though less by time than by total astonishment, was Mrs Stella Dove of Ilfracombe, startled relict of
one William Dove, regarded by his spouse as permanent and
as immortal as the sea which roared or whispered, according
to season, but a stone's throw from her own front door.
William Dove had departed this life in what his acquain-
tances would have called his prime. But he was prime only in
calendar. His demeanour, his emotional range, both were
infantile.

He'd chosen the dinner-table as a setting for his quietus,
and its timing, that short interval between the meat-course
and the dessert. Mrs Dove gave a thought to the apple-
crumble, her Sunday speciality, which at that moment was
cosily cooked in the oven. She was about to rise when she
heard the crash of her husband's dinner-plate as it fell to the
floor. It did not for one second occur to her to berate him for
his carelessness, or for the loss of her precious Sunday Crown
Derby. If Mr Dove crashed his plate to the floor, he must
have had a very good reason for so doing. And as it turned
out, it was plenty good enough. He simply wanted room to
sprawl his arms and his head. He wanted to clear a space for
his dying. Fair enough, Mrs Dove thought later as she stacked
her best dinner-plates and could not count them beyond five.
But what was not so fair was his parting shot. Its tone was no
surprise, for he had used it on her all her married life. That of
reprimand. His last words, muffled by mahogany, but
audible enough, complained yet again that his needs had
not been adequately catered for. 'Why isn't there any pud-
ding?' he had said. And there it was all the time, nestling
in the oven, awaiting its serving. Not fair at all, Mrs Dove
thought. And not only unfair was his leavetaking, but faintly

11

unmemorable, not one that could be quoted in any drawing-room as a token of his intelligence or imagination. The manner of Mr Dove's death was as trivial as the nature of his life which centred all interest exclusively around his own person. But whatever its triviality, it simply wasn't fair, Mrs Dove thought again, as she drew the pouting apple-crumble from the oven. It had shrunk a little, and cringed in its pie-bowl, as if accused of being the cause of death.

When Mrs Dove had finished cleaning the kitchen, she returned to the dining-room tentatively to confirm what she could not for one moment believe. She would not touch him. She kept her distance and stared incredulous at his slumped unmoving body. 'William,' she whispered, half-believing he was sleeping, and terrified of waking him. Then she gathered courage, and shouted his name with steadily growing belief that he would never awake again to berate her for disturbing him. 'William,' she screamed into the empty room, over and over again, and by the time the neighbours arrived, she was screaming for pure joy. The doctor came and confirmed Mrs Dove's widowhood and choroused with the neighbours that poor Mr Dove had died in his prime.

When the screams had subsided and given way to tears, Mrs Dove wondered why she was crying. She could not ascribe her tears to grief, though she was grateful to them, for they looked most becoming under her black funeral veil. Her eyes were wide and questioning, but staring, not with sorrow, but with utter and total astonishment. The effect on her of Mr Dove's passing had been none other than sheer stupefaction that he, who had for so long proclaimed his divine infallibility, had proved to be mortal after all. And moreover, even more mortal than she herself, whose poor attributes he had for so long diminished. With all her shortcomings, Mrs Dove had shamelessly survived him and, when no-one was looking, she smiled into her widow's weeds.

After his death, she awoke each morning with a strange sense of innocence that she did not understand. Later on, when she thought about it, she realised that she was waking without fear, unafraid that there was not a clean shirt for him, or a suitable pair of socks, and this liberation from socks and shirts kindled the beginnings of a decision never to marry again. But the thought was only a passing one. Stella Dove been so long conditioned to the social proprieties of the marital status, that she could not allow herself to dwell on the advantages that could be reaped from the single state. Widowhood was slightly more respectable than sheer spinsterhood. But only marginally so, for both finally spelt rejection. So after not too much thought, Stella Dove decided that she must marry again, if only for form's sake.

To this end, she took herself for morning strolls along Ilfracombe promenade, a path rarely trod with coupled steps. This matinal circuit was a lone trail, and its tempo slow, for most of the trekkers were widowed or retired, exhausted by labour and relationship, and all of them were confident that there was no shame in being seen alone as long as it was morning. Who of the passers-by would know of the unoccupied three-piece suite they had left at home, of the single lamb chop in the refrigerator, or the stark undented second pillow on the creaking double bed? In the mornings on the promenade, one's aloneness did not show, and the walkers were almost cocky with self-confidence. 'Good morning, lovely day,' they said as they passed each other, but rarely stopped to take conversation further, lest the lie of their self-assurance be laid. And many wished good morning to Mrs Dove, and she to them, but no-one stopped, although in desperation, she could sometimes be seen to linger. Then, ashamed of her boldness, she hurried home.

With the onset of winter, she went out less and less, temporarily preferring her health to a husband, though some, she noticed through her drawing-room window, still hopefully blazed the lone, snow-covered trail.

She was given to watching television, particularly favouring programmes concerned with competition. She thought that most of the questions were very childish, and from her armchair she whispered the answers aloud. The prizes were so attractive that the thought crossed her mind that she might apply herself as a competitor. But she was afraid that her neighbours might see her, so she bought competition magazines instead. For a whole year of her widowhood, she applied herself to their questions and answers, coveting the varying booty of Christmas hampers, cars, vacuum cleaners and tool-boxes. In any one week, she had a half a dozen entries safely in the post, and every Friday she would scan the prize-winners' pages of the magazines and fail to find her name. At first she was disappointed, but the act of entering, of filling in the forms, had become so pleasurable that the results were of secondary importance. After a year or so, she became hooked on form-filling, and the highlight of her week was her Monday trip to Ilfracombe post-office where, with infinite care, she posted her sundry entries, slowly, one by one.

It was a Thursday when a stranger called. 'Mrs Dove?' she enquired through the crack allowed her in the door.

Mrs Dove nodded, apprehensive.

'Mrs Stella Dove?' the woman asked again.

'Yes,' Mrs Dove said again. She was very nervous.

'I'm from *Pit your Wits*,' the caller announced, showing her card to prove it. 'May I come in?'

Mrs Dove hesitated. She recalled *Pit your Wits* as one of the titles of the sundry magazines she subscribed to. She could not imagine why this woman was calling on her and feared that she had done some wrong. That she had put *Pit your Wits* into some kind of jeopardy, had damaged their well-earned reputation. She was about to apologise.

'It's good news, Mrs Dove,' the woman said, smiling.

Mrs Dove opened the door wide. The smile relaxed her a little. She was glad the caller was a woman. She could let her into her home without appearing to be too forward. 'Come in,' she said, leading the way into the lounge.

The woman followed, as nervous as Mrs Dove, and hovered around the settee, waiting for her host to settle herself. But Mrs Dove hovered too, and offered a cup of tea, inviting the caller to settle herself while she put the kettle on. She fled to the kitchen, needing very much to be on her own for a while, to try to recall, out of all the first prizes that she had competed for that week, what exact offer *Pit your Wits* had tempted her with. She remembered that one of the magazines had carried a picture of the very latest hoover. She hoped that that was not her prize, for she already had one. She hoped too that it was not a food-mixer. She did not believe in such labour-saving devices. She preferred to mix her cakes by hand. There was a tool-kit too, she remembered, a huge cast-iron box, full of frightening instruments, man's work, a prize that would have confused and embarrassed her. But the woman carried nothing with her, except her handbag, Mrs Dove recalled, so whatever it was that she had scored must be of small proportions and portable. She brewed the tea and took her time setting out the tray. She wanted to postpone her return to the living-room for as long as possible for she was embarrassed by her supposed success and ashamed to be the recipient of its harvest, however small or insignificant.

Meanwhile in the living-room, the woman rehearsed to herself how she would break the news, and as she did so, she thanked God yet again for having landed her this oh so Christian a job of bringing glad tidings wherever she went. And moreover being paid for it. She hoped that her Christian spirit was in no way diluted by its professionalism, but every Sunday she put an extra coin into the church plate just for insurance.

Mrs Dove entered with the tray. 'I'll pour the tea first,' she said quickly, still wary of knowing her winnings. She took her time, pouring the milk slowly, and fussing with the strainer. Then there were the biscuits and the sugar to be organised and, when all was accomplished, there was nothing more to do but to enquire and have declared the purpose of the woman's visit.

But the caller had dried. In her nervousness, each word of her prepared speech had collided meaninglessly with another. She took a gulp of tea, and without putting down her cup, 'You've won first prize,' she spluttered. It did not occur to the visitor that Mrs Dove had applied for at least a dozen first prizes that very week. The visitor was so devoted to her Christian employers that she could not brook any competition, and Mrs Dove was too ashamed to admit her faithless promiscuity.

'Oh how wonderful,' she said, and meant it, even though it might have applied to the cumbersome tool-box.

The visitor opened her bag and handed over a long envelope. 'A Mediterranean cruise,' she announced, stifling the envy in her voice which she knew to be un-Christian. 'For two,' she added, and almost wept with jealousy.

Mrs Dove began to tremble. The concept of a cruise was negotiable only as long as it was fantasy. As a day-dream, it presented no problem. But the reality was too outlandish to accommodate. And one word that the woman had said, or two, Mrs Dove recalled, two words of such sinister overtones, and of such far-fetched proportions, that even in a day-dream, they were barely admissible. 'For two,' the woman had said, and she had salivated each syllable as if it were some kind of extra bonus.

'My poor husband would have loved a cruise,' Mrs Dove said, or rather the words came out of her as if in automatic response to a button pressed by a stranger. Had the words been laid out on a gaming board, they would have been lit with flashing neon, and brittle bells would have pealed on each lying syllable. But in spite of her relief in her widow-hood, it would, in this instance, have been more convenient if Mr Dove were alive. His presence by her side would give her no pleasure, but at least it would publicly give the lie to her loneliness. She had to find a cruise companion. She had at least to find a body to put on her star- or lar-board side.

She opened the gift envelope. Inside were two tickets and a cheque to the value of £250.

'To rig yourself out,' the woman explained, 'For special cruise frocks,' she added, thinking how fat Mrs Dove was, and how no amount of haute couture could fashion her a figure as passable as her own. 'Have you thought of whom you'll take with you?' the woman said. 'You must have lots of friends,' she added as compensation for her recent uncharitable thoughts.

'I'll have to think about it,' Mrs Dove said, meaning that she would once again have to set out on the morning promenade. 'When does it sail?' she asked.

'In three weeks,' the woman said. 'From Southampton. That should give you plenty of time to make arrangements. Oh how I envy you.' She smiled as she heard her words; they were out, exposed in public confession. Envy was only human after all.

'I'm a very lucky woman,' Mrs Dove said, unsure of her luck and wondering what she should wear on the following morning on the lonesome trail. She wished the woman would go away. There were so many things she had to think about. 'Would you like some more tea?' Mrs Dove asked, for politeness' sake, hoping it would be refused.

The woman declined. She too was anxious to leave. She had begun to notice the pretty china in Mrs Dove's cabinet,

the expensive carpeting, wall to wall, the ornate golden
telephone on the painted side-table and she was seething with
resentment against this woman who had everything, and a
cruise on top of it all. It simply wasn't fair. She did not like
her own thoughts for she knew that the Devil had sent them,
and he had no place in her new job that was so full of
charitable notions to which she was by nature so ill-disposed.
Sometimes when she arrived at work in the mornings, she
wanted to set fire to the whole building and reduce to ashes
all the love, goodwill and bountiful grace it was said to
dispense, none of which had ever come her poor single way.
'Oh God,' she whispered to herself, 'pay a little of Your
attention to me. Or I'll bloody well kill You.'

She rose. 'Well I hope you have a lovely time,' she said and
tried with all her heart to mean each word.

'Thank you very much,' Mrs Dove said, ushering her out
with barely concealed haste, but when the woman had gone,
Mrs Dove wished her back again to postpone any thoughts on
her companionless dilemma. She sat down again in her chair
and perused the brochure that accompanied the ticket. On a
simple one-lined map, it outlined the cruise route. The sea
was photographed in a dizzy blinding blue and the ports of
call were gothic in illuminated print. Bordeaux, Marseilles,
Venice, Limassol. She said the words aloud and read the
sight-seeing promises of each stop-over. She declaimed them
loudly into her sitting-room, denying them the silence of
day-dream, the obligatory muteness of fantasy, so that slowly
she was able to equate her own solid person with each single
pleasure-pursuit of the cruise programme. But for the one
factor: that shadowy person by her cruising side, that vague
accessory who stubbornly remained the stuff of dreams. She
thought again of the lonesome trail, but she knew that even if
she encountered a possible companion on the very next
morning, it would take more than three weeks of cunning to
fashion him as helpmeet for her cabin. She sought in her
mind for other alternatives. She had a number of women
friends, widowed like herself, who would have jumped at the
invitation. But Mrs Dove was not a generous woman and
didn't see why she should freely share the fruits of her
competition skills. With a man it would be different. In that
direction there would be some pay-off, at least in the public

17

eye. But to be seen in the companionship of a woman was to be seen to have failed, and actually to give generously for such a public display of failure was bordering on the ridiculous. No, a woman companion was out of the question, and a man as consort so remote a possibility that that, too, could not merit her consideration. Neither could she think of going by herself. There were advantages certainly in being alone and publicly available, but there was the risk that there would be no-one on board who would wish to profit by her availability. It was too big a chance to take.

She collected the tea-things onto the tray and took them into the kitchen. She needed thought-postponement. She knew that all the alternatives she had offered herself were in themselves postponements of a sort, for none of them could she seriously entertain. But each of them was convenient enough as a means of delay, enough to retard that confrontation with that one and only person who could, with all logic if with nothing else, claim the companion role. Mrs Dove's daughter. There was no suitability in such a choice, and certainly no possibility of pay-off, but the option reeked of logic, and was pungent with the smell of duty. How could I be thinking of anybody else? Mrs Dove thought, as she rinsed the cups in the sink, and knew well enough why she had shut her daughter from her mind, logical as that choice might be. There was no safety in it and, almost certainly, no pleasure. In Mrs Dove's mind, it was simply the right thing to do. She refrained from thinking further of the consequences of such an invitation. She would first clear the kitchen, and then return to the living-room. If she dawdled long enough it would be time for the television news, and perhaps a whole evening of programmes that would hold her interest and delay her decision. A large part of Mrs Dove's activity was concerned with postponement and non-confrontation. She relied on external events to make decisions for her, and such events were often forthcoming. But in this instance, it was hard to imagine any happening that would solve the problem of her cruise-mate, that would suddenly transform her daughter into the ideal travelling-companion, that would give tongue to all the unspoken words between them, that would enable the one to look squarely in the other's eye, with resigned if not joyful acceptance. But Mrs Dove shelved such a thought. Even the possibility of a possibility was non-confrontable. As she waited for the television news, she made a concerted effort not to think about her daughter. In her mind she stored a steady list of non-thinkables. Heading the catalogue was her daughter's broken marriage. Mrs Dove spent a few seconds positively putting it out of her mind. As a close second on the list, came the unthinkable Nellie, who was dismissed as swiftly as she was unconsidered. Finally there was her daughter herself, her Alice, so-called for the golden hair she'd been born with. Alice was the supreme and the sublime unthinkable, and by the time the whole catalogue had been diverted, the television announcer had started on the news.

Mrs Dove sat cosily postponed, and was a little irritated when the telephone rang. Irritated, not only for its sheer interruption, but for the identity of the caller whom she knew with total certainty was none other than Alice herself. Mrs Dove could tell by the tone of the ringing, or so she liked to think. Alice was such a threat to poor Mrs Dove's non-confrontation, that even her ringing-tone shrilled with Cassandra-alarm. Mrs Dove reached for the receiver, with fear and suspicion as if it were going to bite her.

'Hullo Mother,' the voice boomed through the wire, and by its cheerful tone, Mrs Dove knew that Nellie stood behind her daughter, and was possibly fondling her ear, and that both were doubtlessly dungareed, deficient of gender. But she shelved those thoughts too, and managed to smile but only because she was invisible.

'Hullo Alice,' she said. 'Are you well?' knowing that she was, and for reasons that were totally unacceptable.

'I'm going back to my own flat,' Alice said, and Mrs Dove wondered why she was saying it with such good cheer, and she allowed herself a small glimmer of hope that her Alice had reverted to normalcy. And with overwhelming gratitude at this possibility, she spilt her prize-winning news, together with the invitation to join her. She tried to ignore the very positive pause on the other end of the line, and to underrate the over-enthusiasm of the acceptance when it finally came. Alice said she would call on her the following evening after she had settled in her own flat.

The news was almost finished by the time Mrs Dove put

down the phone, and she was faced with a decision that had
been made outside herself, with an invitation that had issued
itself of its own accord. The time had come not to think about
it. But one thought she could not dismiss, the small faint hope
that amongst her daughter's dungareed construction-worker's
luggage, amongst all the accoutrements of mis-routed sisterhood, there lay one frock, one simple pretty frock, floral
perhaps, with puffed sleeves, a Peter Pan collar and, perhaps,
though she must not be too greedy, a pretty hair-ribbon,
Nellie-concealed, in little Alice's spongebag. Mrs Dove looked
again at the cruise brochure, and its promise, line by line, of
exotic romance, and all of it in front of other people, and she
trembled with the terror of it all.

Three weeks later, Mrs Dove and her daughter changed
trains at Waterloo station and boarded the Southampton
express. Alice shrugged off all proffered help from porters and
humped the luggage alone. She strode in front of her mother
like a stranger. Mrs Dove was happy to lag behind, denying
relationship. Not a word had passed between them since their
departure from Ilfracombe, and Mrs Dove already wanted to
go back home. She watched her daughter's dungareed bottom
as it asserted its despotic way through the polite and portered
cruise-passengers. She recalled the brochure's suggestion that
travellers should dress for dinner, and she wondered what
bloody-minded rig-out her Alice had in mind to shame her
with.
   They settled into the compartment, the cases firmly
wedged between them. Mrs Dove very much wanted to cry.
   Alice stared straight ahead of her, her lips tight, her skin
taut, her teeth clenched, her whole body an armoury of
corkage to stop up her pain. She ached for Nellie, whom, in a
moment of reason, she had left; she ached too for Richard
who, in a like moment of reason, had left *her*. She writhed in a
terrible confusion. Out of the corner of her eye, she viewed
the stranger seated next to their luggage and she longed for
some concrete proof of their relationship.
   For her part, Mrs Dove dared not look anywhere, except
into her unaccusing lap, but she felt her daughter's glance,
and longed to stretch out her hand, and, even without
looking, to touch her. But the distance between them was

seven seas, and language was a Babel. So they remained, the two of them, for the hour's journey to the coast, silent and unreachable.

Further down the carriage, Ellen Walsh and Alice Pickering were tweeting like two little birds, covering their nervousness with inconsequential chatter. For both women were apprehensive, fully aware of the great adventure that was in store.

'Ellen,' Alice ventured after a pause, 'you won't ... well, you won't leave me alone, will you?'

Ellen might well have asked the same of Alice, but her lack of self-confidence was not for confession. She squeezed Alice's arm. 'We'll look after each other,' she said.

As the train pulled into the station, they caught sight of the two huge funnels of their ship.

'I'm frightened,' Alice said and, though Ellen shared her fear, she took care not to show it. She fervently hoped that they would quickly find a man on board who would look after them both. Two men, perhaps, Ellen dared to hope, though secretly she held out little hope for Alice, who was so Pickering-prim.

'You must let yourself go,' Ellen said, rather roughly. 'You must let your hair down, Alice.'

Alice didn't know what Ellen was talking about and she clutched at her arm as they left the train.

'Don't worry,' Ellen said, 'once we're on board, everything will be fine.'

She tried to inject some confidence into her voice. Secretly she wished that Thomas was with her, or even Walsh, and Alice, too, indulged in a small Pickering-longing, and hoped that Ellen couldn't read her thoughts.

The passengers boarded. Ellen and Alice took their first terrified steps into the unknown, followed by the silent pair of Doves, who mounted the gangway to the ship as if it were the ladder to the guillotine.

CHAPTER THREE

An uninvited guest

Ellen and Alice were to share a cabin, and it was not until the steward had deposited their bags by their beds, and declared himself available at all times for the least service, and had shut the door firmly behind him, that the two women realised their sudden isolation. The confinement of the small cabin unnerved them both and, though private, was completely lacking in any privacy. They realised that, despite their close neighbourliness over so many years, there was little intimacy between them. They did not know each other's clothes, much less each other's bodies. Over the years neither washing-line had forfeited any secrets. Both Ellen and Alice had dried their underwear indoors. Pickering and Walsh and, for a while, the short-lived Thomas, had been sartorially displayed outdoors, as if their secrets were not worth the keeping.

Alice and Ellen turned their backs on each other, like two strangers, and laid their cases on their beds. For both women the unpacking itself would be a revelation. Ellen decided to do it blatantly, and thus relieve the tension in her friend. But Alice had the same intention, and both women flung their lingerie aside with the nonchalance that would have been proper in a teenager. On closer side-long glances, its style was teenage too. The departed trio of Pickering, Walsh and Thomas would never have seen the like of it. Both women had clearly and separately decided that widowhood represented a departure from the norm. Wherever that new way was to lead was unknown and unquestioned, but, whatever its destination, the journey required a new form of equipment. Over the 'decent' years Ellen and Alice had spent together, each had secretly collected what could only be called a second trousseau, and their small and gentle gleanings now lay tissued on their separate beds. Ellen and Alice almost blushed to look at them. They heard a knock on their door, and the call that dinner would be served in half an hour. They withdrew their dinner dresses from the suitcases and draped them over the beds.

'That's pretty,' Ellen said, looking at Alice's blue chiffon. Much too young, she thought, with that Peter Pan collar and puff sleeves. She felt a little sorry for her.

'I like yours too,' Alice was saying, though red was hardly Ellen's colour, she thought, and a little daring for her age. She began to pity her.

'You can use the bathroom first,' Ellen said. 'I'll finish my unpacking.

Ellen was glad to be on her own for a while. Neither of them had made a secret of their lingerie, but what that lingerie covered was an altogether different matter, and could not so easily be flaunted. Ellen was better acquainted with her new underwear than with her body that had belonged to her for so many years. She needed to take a look at it, to examine its flaws, its assets, before deciding whether or not it was fit for display. And in the bathroom, Alice was doing exactly the same. Ellen had the advantage of a full-length mirror, while Alice had to make do with the small square of glass over the sink. So Alice's body-information was gleaned from a top-shot angle and thus distorted, and possibly to her advantage, while Ellen was faced with the truth of a bold unlit full-frontal. At first, she was wary of looking, and to overcome her shyness, she blindly covered her hips and thighs with a towel, with the intention of a self-estimation by instalments. Alice was doing likewise, though her lack of equipment, as well as her shyness, dictated such a manoeuvre.

Ellen was astonished. She had expected worse. She had no means of comparison. She rarely saw her sister, and certainly never unclothed. But what she saw pleased her. Her breasts, though fallen, were of equal and modest size. They looked as if they could do with a little ironing, but apart from that, they were easy enough on the eye. She would have no shame of her upper parts. The lower section was a different matter. In that quarter, more than any other, age had notched the passing years. The curtain of stomach, the mottled drape of thigh, the battleground of Walsh and Thomas invasion, she now reclaimed as her own, and covered it again for its protection. Her legs and her feet were available for anyone's viewing. She decided she would fashion her dressing and undressing accordingly.

In the bathroom, Alice was coming to similar conclusions. Age had taken its toll on the Pickering field, now ploughed over and left fallow. There had been no other invader, Pickering's incursion had been unaggressive enough. Alice's scars, unlike Ellen's, belonged more to nature than man's mismanagement. She patted her stomach, and recalled with acute astonishment that once it had lodged two children. Then she had to think of how they had come there and she writhed with its recall. Poor Pickering, she said to herself. He had found it faintly disgusting as well.

She knocked on the bathroom door to warn Ellen of her reappearance.

'Just a minute,' Ellen said, reaching for her dressing-gown. When Alice appeared she was similarly clothed. Slowly the shyness between them, that shyness that has nothing to do with gender, was evaporating. Ellen went to the bathroom while Alice dressed, and Alice then offered to make up in the bathroom while Ellen dressed for dinner. It was a neat arrangement that would see them through the twenty-one days of their cruising.

No such neat arrangement in the Dove cote. While her mother was in the bathroom, Alice Dove impatiently paced the cabin. Her mother heard the trekking boots stomping outside, and hurried with her toilet. She had hoped to take a shower, but Alice's patience clearly would not have stretched to that. So she flannelled and powdered herself quickly, fearful of the ominous pacing outside. As she came out of the bathroom, Alice passed inside without a word, and Mrs Dove sat at the dressing-table and tried to take her mind off her mind. She stared at her new evening-dress hanging over the cabin door. It was a white imitation-silk covered with tiny spring flowers. Mrs Dove knew that her daughter would laugh at it. She was deeply anxious as to what Alice would wear. Certainly it was nothing that needed hanging, for she had not yet fully unpacked. Mrs Dove was sorely tempted to peek inside Alice's suitcase for the hoped-for glimpse of feminine attire, but she was frightened that Alice would surprise her from the bathroom. She began to make-up her face and, through the mirror, she saw her daughter enter the cabin, her long golden hair loose about her shoulders. Mrs Dove wanted to cry for joy. The hair had been carefully brushed and looked dressed for an occasion. She was hopeful. She kept her eyes on the mirror and saw Alice open her case and extract a tissued package, through which she could define the colour of primrose. Again hope surged in her. Until Alice removed the tissue and held out a pair of new dungarees, of pale yellow silk it was true, but dungarees withal.

'That's pretty,' Mrs Dove said into the mirror, surprised by her own words for they were the first that had passed between them since leaving Ilfracombe. She saw the amazed look on her daughter's face. Her mother's approval was so unexpected, she didn't know how to handle it, or even whether she wanted it at all. She pulled her hair into a tight angry knot, and spitefully pinned it on top of her head. Mrs Dove did not open her mouth again.

She put on her new dress and hoped that Alice would make no comment. But Alice knew all about approval and otherwise. Everything between them was wrong, every word, sub-titled to the other's need, every gesture, mis-read in the other's projection, every glance un-met, however yearning. Silent and separate, they made their way to the dining-room. The head waiter assigned them to a corner table and, even before sitting down, Alice looked defiantly at her mother and, in unnatural and rough tones, she ordered a pint of beer. Mrs Dove stared at the daisies on her dress, and she remembered the daisy chains she had made as a child, and all that laughter and all that joy, so many heart-aches ago.

When Ellen and Alice were ready, they admired each other's look, and hesitated before going to the dining-room. They were both unused to company and were wary of strangers. 'I daren't think that we may have to sit with others at our table,' Alice said, though she nourished a small hope that this would be the case. Sometimes she ran out of things to say to Ellen and she was embarrassed by the silences between them. She had to admit that Ellen frightened her a little. Ellen seemed to have done so much more with her life than she. Yet when she tried to examine what those extras were, she found it hard to understand how their lives had been so different. They had both lived in identical houses, in a style tailored to their husbands' incomes which they knew were equal. They'd both had two children, a boy and a girl apiece; they'd had summers together in the same boarding house at Ilfracombe, year after year until the children had gone their own ways. Throughout their married lives, Alice had kept her eye on her friend and had been satisfied with the dull balance of their experience. The single unbalancing factor was Thomas. It was true that Alice hadn't known a second time round, but looking at Thomas cutting the hedge or about the house did not give her the impression that he could even marginally enrich someone's experience. She couldn't imagine what Ellen and he talked about or did together. But she did not want to dwell on that, for she feared what it might be, and she knew too that that was the weight that tipped the balance. She knew it, because after they were married Ellen's washing line was bare, as if both were now entitled to indoor drying, as she and Pickering had been in their first few months together. She'd never talked to Ellen about Thomas, and now she wondered whether it would be a proper subject of conversation to fill the silences between them. Ellen was not likely to take offence. Thomas had gone, along with the other hedge-cutters, and Ellen hadn't even given him a 'decent' year. She surely would not be averse to talking about him. So that's what Alice had in mind, as a filler for awkward pauses.

But when they reached the dining-room, it was clear that no conversation would be possible, least of all that of intimate kind. For a Palm Court orchestra was playing, and at a volume that indicated that the audience was deaf. And a look around the dining-room suggested that this was quite probably the case, for Ellen Walsh and Alice Pickering, with one hundred and twenty-six years between them, were almost the babies of the party.

A waiter met them at the entrance and yelled at them to follow him. He led them to a table at the far end of the room where the decibel rate was mercifully lower, so that intermittent conversation would have been possible. But certainly none of the intimate kind, for their table was already occupied. A single gentleman, of dignified appearance, was tucking his napkin into his frilled shirt-front. He rose as they approached, and held each of their chairs as the ladies took their seats. The waiter fled before any questions could be asked. Not that Ellen or Alice would have dreamed of complaining even though there might have been reasonable grounds for reproach.

'I'm Victor Bowers.' The man put out his hand.

The women looked at each other. 'Go on, Ellen,' Alice said timidly, and she wondered why she had asked Ellen to take the initiative. And quickly she regretted it, so she thrust out her hand and put it in his. 'I'm Alice Pickering,' she quivered, and for good measure, 'and this is my friend Ellen ... er ...' She wasn't sure whose widow Ellen regarded herself, and she wished then that she had never opened her mouth.

'I haven't lost my tongue.' Alice saw Ellen mouth through the din, and though she didn't hear the words, she knew from the curl of Ellen's lip that they were a reprimand.

'I'm Ellen Head,' Ellen shouted, giving the man her hand.

Now Alice was thoroughly confused. She knew Head to be Ellen's maiden name, and in its declaration she heard a faint echo of betrayal. And treachery twice over, if Thomas had been anything more than a hedge-cutter. How *could* she? Alice thought. It was as if, in offering her hand to this stranger, she had more than introduced herself. She had openly declared her availability, and the report that she had served no other master. Alice tried on her own baptism. Alice Brewster. The image that that name framed was blurred. It was young, that's all she could decipher, and its colour was sepia. She saw no point in restoring it. In any case, Pickering had been a name harder to come by than her given one, and it would be to diminish achievement if she relinquished it now. She was Pickering's woman, as was right and proper, as right and as proper as Ellen was Walsh's, and she wondered whether her friend had been influenced by all the talk that was going round about women's liberation. She shuddered at the thought of it. 'Alice Pickering,' she said again to the man, and though neither he nor Ellen could hear her, she could hear it well enough, and it was by way of self-assurance.

'I hope you don't mind if we share a table,' Mr Bowers said as soon as there was an interval in the music. 'If you wish to be alone, I could have a word with the steward,' he offered.

'Not at all,' Ellen said without any consultation with her friend, 'you are very welcome I'm sure.' She spoke as if the table were hers and Mr Bowers her guest. Alice thought it was ill-mannered, so she said, 'Are you sure *you* don't mind?' but the band had restarted, and her attempt at courtesy was drowned by the drums.

The three of them studied the menu. Alice was appalled to notice that all the dishes were written in French, and the English translation was in such small type as to be unreadable. Out of vanity, she had not brought her glasses, and she knew that Ellen's, too, lay on their dressing-table.

Mr Bowers' glasses were expensive tortoiseshell, Ellen had noticed, and these he'd pushed up to his forehead to read the menu with greater ease. 'The roast beef looks exciting,' he shouted.

'I think I'll have that too,' Ellen said. And so did Alice, for she could see no other choice.

'Would you take a little wine with me?' Mr Bowers said. 'I'd be happy to invite you.'

'That would be very kind of you I'm sure,' Ellen said quickly, fearing that Alice might refuse, for Alice could be a little priggish at times.

Mr Bowers called the wine-waiter, and as he studied the list, the band stopped, or rather, it came to the end of its tune and didn't start again. The diners shifted in their chairs, not knowing how to deal with the sudden silence. They tested their voices in whispers, mindful of a possible reprise from the band – the brochures had featured the small orchestra with much earnestness as a cruise bonus not to be taken for granted – but the players had already risen from their seats and were making their way towards the bar. It was now in legal order for the diners to converse. But still they talked in whispers as if not to disturb the marvel of their unaccustomed and lavish surroundings. Alice was nervous. She could think of nothing to say, and she was glad that Ellen was there to keep Mr Bowers happy. For happy he must be kept, she thought. He was about to buy them a bottle of wine, and nothing was for nothing.

'Are you from London?' Ellen was saying, and Alice wondered why she hadn't thought of that question herself. It was such an obvious enquiry, and showed interest without inquisitiveness.

'I live in Wiltshire,' he said. 'In the country. And you?'

'We're from London,' Alice put in her bid. 'We're neighbours.'

The waiter uncorked the bottle, poured a little into Mr Bowers' glass and waited for his verdict. Mr Bowers dismissed the offer. He trusted the label, he said, and Alice was very impressed, and so was Ellen but she took greater pains to hide it.

'Have you been on a cruise before, Mrs Pickering?' Mr Bowers was aware that he must share his attentions.

She shook her head.

'And you, Mrs Head?'

Alice giggled, and Ellen shifted nervously in her seat.

'Have I said anything untoward?' Mr Bowers asked. 'Oh I'm sorry, perhaps it's Miss Head.'

Serves you right Ellen Walsh, Alice thought. Now he'll think you're a spinster.

'Head is my maiden name.' Ellen rallied. 'I was married. But now I'm a widow. Twice widowed in fact,' she added, staring at Alice who could muster only one funeral in her time.

Mr Bowers felt he should offer his condolences, so mighty was Ellen's declaration, but instead he offered her his own widowhood. 'My dear wife died only a month ago.'

Alice was faintly offended. Was it only men who were entitled to the 'decent' year?

'We had booked this cruise together,' he said. 'She was so looking forward to it. When she died, I decided to go on my own. In her memory, as it were.'

So Alice forgave him. Pickering would have done the same.

'It's much harder for a man to be on his own,' Ellen said, and Alice thought it sounded like a proposal, and she was glad she hadn't thought of saying it. She didn't want Mr Bowers to think badly of Ellen, and by reflection, of herself. He had, after all, bought them a bottle of wine. They really must be grateful.

'I'm getting used to it,' he said. 'One has to.'

There was a pause then, and even Ellen could find nothing to fill it though Alice saw her brows furrowing, scratching in her mind for something to say. Alice wished the band would return. Then the waiter came with the roast beef trolley, and with his air of business and array of tools, promised some form of spectator-occupation. Ellen thought that her own home-made beef looked a lot more succulent, but she had to acknowledge that this presentation was superior.

'I hope it's as good as yours, Ellen,' Alice said, and to Mr Bowers, 'Roast beef is Ellen's speciality.' She suddenly felt very protective of Ellen and all that independent 'Head' nonsense.

'My wife made a great roast beef,' Mr Bowers said, and Alice regretted her testimonial.

The waiter served them according to their tastes and appetite, a sliver of medium for Mr Bowers, and well-done slices for the ladies. When each was served, Mr Bowers raised his glass. 'What shall we drink to?' he asked.

'To our dear departed,' Ellen said, and Alice thought that was somewhat tasteless, since it seemed unfair to equate a month-long sorrow with ones that had endured for over a year. But Mr Bowers took no offence. 'We must drink to the living too,' he said. 'To us, and the years that are left to us.'

They drank, and Alice was pleased that they would start on their meal, the quality of which could be a subject of conversation. But Ellen seemed quite happy to occupy herself with the food, and so did Mr Bowers.

'This wine is delicious,' Alice said, knowing that gratitude was always a welcome time-filler.

'Thank you very much,' Ellen said, and Alice was a little piqued, because the theme of gratitude could be spun out endlessly as long as one refrained from a positive 'thank you.' But to speak those words aloud was to close the conversation once and for all.

'The meat is good too,' Alice tried once more, but there were no takers on that one, except into the mouth. So Alice gave up and turned to her dinner as the others were doing. Between mouthfuls she looked around the dining-room. There were many more women than men and most of them seemed coupled. Two women sat together at a corner-table, but they looked like two singles, Alice thought, so public was the strangers' silence between them. And one of them was actually wearing trousers. Alice turned her head away. Such attire was lacking in respect, she thought. Mr Bowers, sitting on his own, had advertised himself as single, and Alice thought that only a man could get away with it. A woman would never come alone on a cruise, even if her husband was only a month-long dead, and she were sailing in his memory. The public would never allow such treachery, and she would die of the shame of it. She thought it was all rather unfair, and she thought, too, that she mustn't have thoughts like that or she would get like Ellen and start introducing herself as Miss Brewster. Surreptitiously she slapped her hand. It was naughty to have such thoughts. They could only lead to confusion.

'Perhaps we should take a turn about deck after dinner,' Mr Bowers suddenly said.

'A little fresh air would do us good,' Ellen said, and Alice was pleased that Ellen had defined in advance the exact purpose of their promenade. She didn't want Mr Bowers to be getting any ideas, though she dared not think what sort of ideas she forbade him, for she knew that they were sinful. And full of pleasure. 'Alice Pickering,' she murmured to herself. 'What on earth is happening to you?' She thought it must be Ellen's bad influence, due to that extra experience she'd had with that Thomas man.

'Fresh air is good for you,' she echoed Ellen, underlining its absence of sin, and knowing that what was good for you was rarely pleasurable. Pickering used to say that every time he took his ulcer medicine. Suddenly she missed him, the sheer habit of him, the utter predictability of his presence, dull but infinitely secure. She wondered why it was the women who so often outlived their menfolk. She had been used to thinking that men worked harder and had greater responsibilities. She had always accepted that explanation. Now she dared to wonder whether women survived because they were stronger, superior even. She bit on her tongue. It was a blasphemous thought. Her Pickering had been a hard worker and he had always known the answer to everything. It's true that she found out sometimes that he was wrong, but everyone is entitled to make mistakes. But lots of mistakes, like Pickering? She tried to think of other matters. She really needed some fresh air to clear her head of such treacherous thoughts, and she was relieved when the waiter came to take away their plates, and to wheel over the dessert trolley. Once at the table, he whispered that coffee would be served in the lounge as if only their table were to be party to such information, a whisper he would carry to all the other tables and leave each guest with a sense of privilege.

It was easier to exercise choice of dessert, since it was there on the trolley for all to view, with or without glasses. Alice chose a chocolate mousse, making a quick decision, though she would have liked longer to deliberate, but she felt it was discourteous to keep the waiter waiting. Ellen however felt no such compunction. She dillied and dallied between the chocolate layer cake and the charlotte russe, then for no reason decided on a cherry tart with cream. Mr Bowers echoed the same choice and Alice felt a sudden wallflower. 'You can taste my chocolate mousse,' she offered, re-edging herself into the party. But Mr Bowers was allergic to chocolate, he said, and Ellen said that she wasn't partial to pap food. Alice felt herself flushing. She could see right through Ellen. She knew what her so-called friend was doing. Ellen was trying to tell Mr Bowers that all her teeth were her own; that she could still manage the hard crust of a cherry tart, thank you very much, and that she was not yet reduced to mousses like some she could mention. Alice watched Mr Bowers as he chewed without difficulty on the hard crust, and then at Ellen who was doing likewise. She felt very isolated.

'I make patchwork quilts,' she said suddenly, breaking the silence with her shattering irrelevancy. Yet for her, the remark was highly pertinent. The talent of quilting was of far greater worth than immoveable molars. Mr Bowers looked up from his crust and smiled at her. Ellen looked up at her friend and giggled, then returned to her cherry pie. Alice missed Pickering again, yet in all honesty, she couldn't imagine how he would have lent her support at the table. She had been asserting herself with her talk of quilting, and Pickering wouldn't have liked that at all. She was deeply confused, and had it in mind to skip the coffee in the whispering lounge, along with the health-giving promenade, and return to her cabin, and in Ellen's absence conduct a little board-meeting with herself. Yes, she decided, that's what she would do.

'I'm rather tired,' she said. 'I think I'll make an early night. I shan't have coffee. It will keep me awake.'

'No promenade, Mrs Pickering?' Mr Bowers asked politely.

Alice was glad that he had asked, even though she detected little pleading in his question. She noted too that Ellen refrained from persuasion. 'I'm really rather tired,' she said again.

Other guests were leaving the dining-room, and Mr Bowers and the ladies followed them. Alice excused herself and hurried to the cabin. She wanted to be alone and in silence, in order to marshal her thoughts before they dissolved in her confusion. She sat on her bed. Alone now, and in the silence around her, she did not know how to begin. Should she talk to herself aloud? Shout even? Put on all the lights so that she could *see* her words and thus more clearly understand them? 'Pickering,' she whispered for openers. But the name did little to re-assure her. Throughout her 'decent' year, her Pickering feelings had been frightfully confused. Even on the morning of his funeral, she had woken up excited at the thought of showing off her new black hat. The purpose of its exhibition was of secondary concern. She had managed to weep at the funeral, but she had to acknowledge that attendance at a burial was in itself a weepy event, even if the dear departed were a stranger. It was all those dusty words of the vicar, the thud of earth, the last journey with its wasteful luggage of flowers, and all the other people who were weeping in obedient chorus. The house seemed quiet without him, but she'd kept the wireless on all day. Weeks after he'd died, she was ironing and a sudden spark flashed from the plug. The realisation that it was a fuse, man's work, had inspired her first genuine tear, and she shed it gratefully, and let it breed, so that she cried long and loud for many hours. Afterwards she had felt much better, for she was beginning to wonder whether she was callous and cold. She hoped she would cry for him again, and again and again, until the passing of time would blunt her loss. But by the time the next fuse blew – one day when she was hoovering – she had already learned to mend it, and no tears obliged. She felt lonely sometimes, but she kept remembering that she had felt much lonelier during her marriage, especially after the children had left home. When she was married, she didn't *expect* to be lonely, not with a man at your table, and lying nightly by your side. But now, with Pickering's passing, her expectations had been buried

34

too, and with them, a large measure of her loneliness. In her kitchen, she thought of Ellen next door, sitting like herself, reading a book perhaps, or knitting as she herself was doing, and she wondered whether she too entertained such thoughts. And whether she too felt guilty. Even when her birthday came round once more, four months after Pickering's death, she did not rise from her bed with the sad thought of his absence. She told herself that she had reached the age of 62, that she was not yet an old woman, that she was young enough even to marry again. And with this suggestion, she took herself to the hairdresser's, and treated herself to a café tea, and that night she had taken a hot-water-bottle to bed, and a new paper-back novel. Propped up against her pillows, sipping from a mug of hot chocolate, she had indulged in her first Pickering thought for many weeks, but only in connection with her earlier thoughts of re-marriage. As the months passed, her every act became one of unconscious self-investigation. She read many novels, and often found her own fears and guilts inside them, dignified and legalised by hard covers. She began to venture alone into cinemas and cafés, and the occassional museum. She even joined a women's guild. Each evening, when she returned from her single sorties, she felt somehow guilty, not because a hot dinner wasn't ready for Pickering, but that there was no duty to be done at all. What she missed above all was duty, and Pickering was usually its name. So it was with his shirts that she no longer ironed, with his socks that she no longer darned. She missed him in the minutiae, but she did not miss the doctrine of wifehood, and a habit is harder to break than a principle. Over the course of her 'decent' year, she grew in some small and hidden splendour, and she was always ashamed that she could do it only because Pickering wasn't there.

Now as she sat on her cabin bed, she wondered what Ellen was doing, and whether, whatever it was, it was on Mr Bowers' arm. She felt a pang of jealousy. When Ellen returned to the cabin, she would not gratify her with questions of how the rest of her evening had been spent. She would pretend to be asleep, and by morning, whatever story Ellen chose to tell, real or imagined, would have lost its edge. She tried to examine her jealousy and had to conclude it was not of the fact but of the fiction. She didn't covet Mr Bowers at all; she was jealous solely of the principle.

There was a knock on the door.

'Come in,' she said, glad that her dangerous thoughts were to be interrupted. A steward poked his head around the door. 'May I prepare the beds?' he said. She nodded.

Afterwards, when the episode was all over, and all untellable, she recalled that she was uneasy with the way he'd peered around the cabin door. It was an unofficial gesture, she had thought, an illegitimate one, as if his request had nothing to do with his calling. As he came in, shutting the door behind him, she recognised him as their waiter at table, the one who'd whispered about the coffee, and she thought it strange that a waiter should double as a steward. She felt uneasy and wished that Ellen would come back. She thought she might ask the steward to return later, but he was already at Ellen's bed, turning down the counterpane. The thought crossed her mind that she should go into the bathroom and lock herself in until his domestic duties were done. But she thought that it would be rude to leave him alone in the cabin. It would be an act of contempt if she were to ignore his presence. It would hint of snobbery and disdain of his station. So she sat there watching him, trying not to notice his ham-fisted folding, his clear unacquaintance with bed-making skills. When he finished, he turned to look at her, and Alice's knees trembled. He's only looking, she said to herself. A cat can look at a king. She rose from her bed so that he could get on with it, but her purpose was escape which she now knew to be futile. She was certain that this man was no steward, that moreover he was probably as illegal in a dining-room as he was in a cabin. She thought of Pickering, and for the first time in many months she missed him with a sudden and terrifying longing.

He stared at her, unsmiling, then came towards her. She stood aside, still protesting to herself her groundless belief in his domestic calling. He placed his hands on her shoulder and pressed her down to the bed. As she opened her mouth to scream he placed his hand over it. 'It will be better for you if you keep quiet,' he whispered. 'This is not going to take very long.'

She was not clear in her mind what the 'this' was he was

referring to, whether to her rape or her murder. The brevity he promised her could have referred to either. Out of the confusion of her thoughts, out of the jungle of her terror and her panic, there was a small clearing of relief. The recollection that she was wearing clean underwear. It did not necessarily make her feel any easier but she was certain that, had she not changed before dinner, her shame would have been compounded. She prayed again for Ellen's swift return, and then quickly reprayed for her absence, for she did not want Ellen to view her fall. If she lived to tell her tale, she swore to herself, she would never tell it, not to Ellen, not to anybody and hopefully not even to herself, for she had it in mind to forget it, whatever it was to be, to erase it from memory, to recall it, if at all, solely as a nightmare, and she shut her eyes so that she would not see whatever it was he had in mind and prayed that she might live to forget it.

She felt him lifting her legs onto the bed. Then he gripped her ankles. Although his hold was firm, she felt a tenderness in his hands. She now believed that he would not kill her, that he would rape her only, and for that she almost thanked him. As he spread her legs, she tried to recall the last time she had lain in a similar receiving position. She thought inevitably of Pickering, since he had been the only donor in her life, but she could no longer envisage their congress. She blushed at the thought of it. It was so long ago; it belonged to so alien a time. All she could remember was her patent lack of skill in the part. She hoped the waiter would forgive her ineptitude and ascribe it to a lack of recent practice. She didn't want him to be cross with her, else he might think of some other measure to satisfy his appetites. She could think of nothing positive to do to accommodate him, so she decided to lie quite still and let him do what he wished with her, and hope that, whatever it was, it was not fatal. She felt her legs parting and it was then that terror struck her.

Her body froze, but without rigidity. She shivered with the sheer cold of her fear. Each separate part of her body trembled. She dreaded that he might order her to keep still, and she longed for some warmth, even if it had to be his own body, to cover her. She longed for it, she willed it, but all she felt of him was his trouser serge against her inner knee. Even

37

his hands had left her ankles. She heard an unzipping and a great bile rose in her throat.

'Cover me,' she pleaded. She felt she could withstand anything if only she were warm, but the separation between them increased as the trouser serge left her knee. A cold hand touched her, and then something very hot. But it had nothing to do with heat. She clenched her fists, her eyes, her shoulders, her lips, in an attempt to still her tremblings, as he pumped away, humming and talking to himself, as if he were alone.

She lay, her eyes tightly shut, trying to recall how long Pickering had taken with his performance. But she could barely recall the act itself, leave alone its timing. For some reason she found her assailant's vocal accompaniment more offensive than the performance itself. Suddenly he began to sing, louder and louder, in gutter words she tried not to hear. But he put his mouth to her ear, and whispered them long and loud, pumping away all the time, and Alice was horrified at the sudden pleasure the words sang to her. Her body became warm and yielding, and she wept for poor Pickering who never in a lifetime had so roused her. She listened to every syllable that he dribbled into her ear, and to its rhythmic and regular repetition. She had a sudden urge to raise her knees from the bed, but she was conscious that it would be a gesture of immodest pleasure forbidden to a woman even in the most legitimate of couplings. She half hoped that he would finish quickly so that she would not shame herself in front of him. She'd heard tell about climax, or rather she had read about it. Such a word was not for oral exchange. She didn't quite know what it was, but in the novels it sounded sinfully pleasurable. The written word was orgasm; she had to spell it in her mind for it was unspeakable even to oneself, and she wondered now whether her body's present feelings translated that divine and terrible lettering. She thought her trembling fragile frame would break in two.

Suddenly his last raging syllable hissed through her body and held its note for a long time. He rose from the bed, and she heard a zipping once more.

'There,' he said, 'that wasn't too bad, was it? If you're a good girl, I'll come again some time.'

She heard the cabin door close, but she did not open her

eyes for a long while. She was listening to the whisperings still echoing in her ear, and knowing that she was now alone, she felt free to relish them. When, after a while, she opened her eyes, she sniffed a lingering smell of brilliantine, and it seemed to her right and proper that that was the exact smell of the words still throbbing in her ear.

She got up from the bed and looked at the crumpled counterpane. She was anxious that Ellen should find no evidence of her terrible adventure that had turned out to be more adventurous than terrible. She was ashamed of such thoughts and she thought of Pickering again and begged him to forgive her. As she straightened her dress, she remembered the cold that had at first suffused her body, the icy chill of it, and she was suddenly angry, and the thought passed through her mind that she should go straightway to some authority and report his monstrous act. But she hesitated. No one would believe her. They would look at her ageing hungry body and utter words like fantasy. Of course they *could* believe her, and counter her accusation with the suggestion that she had asked for it. The waiter would confirm that there had been no struggle, that she was waiting for him in her cabin, even that she had winked at him while he was serving her chocolate mousse, that he had only obliged her with his service in much the same way as he would take her tea in the morning. Oh my God, Alice thought, suddenly envisaging that possibility. He might well say something to Ellen, and Ellen must never know. Never, never. Then suddenly she thought she might confide it all to Ellen. Ellen would know what to do. She'd go and report it herself on her friend's behalf, full of anger and righteous indignation, but when faced with their suggestions of collusion, she might well join their ranks. There were three more weeks of Ellen to accommodate, and in the same cabin, reeking with treachery. Alice began to cry. She realised she did not have the courage to take any action whatsoever, and she feared that by not doing so, he would take it as an open invitation to come again as he had threatened. She took a step towards the cabin door, but she thought now that she had left it too late for report, that a genuine rape would be screamed abroad in the fleeing shadow of the attacker. She felt suddenly very dirty, and thought that she might take a bath in an effort to cleanse her shame. But Ellen might return and wonder what she was doing taking a second bath within a matter of hours. Bugger Ellen, she thought, though she did not say it aloud, and she ran to the bathroom and locked the door behind her.

She did not look at her body as she quickly washed it down. She splashed her face with cold water, rinsing out of her ears those beautiful syllables, which she now heard as filthy and foul. Her body sweated with her rage, with herself as prime target. No. She would tell nobody, she decided. What he had done was his own poor and cruel sickness. What she had done, or rather, what she had felt, was her own shame. She rushed to her bed, sweeping the offending counterpane onto the floor and pulled the blanket over her head. She heard Ellen creep into the cabin and call her name. She pretended to be sleeping. She had no appetite for Ellen's nocturnal adventures. She was too sated with her own.

CHAPTER FOUR

A change of quarters

In the morning, Mrs Dove woke after a restless night. She herself had retired early enough, though her daughter had returned to their cabin immediately after dinner. Mrs Dove had felt silly sitting there all alone, and she wondered how she could possibly weather the next three weeks with Alice in such a fractious frame of mind. She was angry too at their dinner placing. They seemed to be the only pair sitting alone and she could not help but blame Alice's flagrantly irregular attire for their punitive isolation. She had noticed that there had been another pair of women who had entered the dining-room later than they, and they had been placed in the company of a single gentleman who had actually taken one of the ladies on an after-dinner promenade. It was only because both women were suitably dressed. Mrs Dove tried not to hate her daughter.

She looked over at Alice's bed. The yellow dungarees were on the floor. The suit-case was open, and its contents ruffled, with promises of many more dungarees to come. Mrs Dove crept out of bed and checked that Alice was still sleeping. She tip-toed to the case and knelt down beside it. Her sad hands trembled over its trousered layers. At the very bottom of the case, the sight of some tissue paper kindled a small hope in her heart. It covered a length of cerise silk, very long, it seemed, and a beautiful colour, Mrs Dove thought, absolutely right for her little Alice with the long golden hair. She dared to investigate further, praying that it was not trouser-divided. She found the hem, and fingered slowly round its whole circuit, and found its perimeter blissfully unbroken. And inside the tissue packaging was a small silk purse of the same cerise colour. Mrs Dove dared to open it. Inside she felt the unmistakeable shape of a lipstick and powder compact. One

41

secret concealed inside another. Her heart almost burst with hoping. She looked at her daughter's sleeping face, and she knew that Alice's hopes too, all of them, were pinned on that tissued sanctuary, hidden from everyone's view, even its fearful owner's, lest its appropriate appearance, ripely-timed, would never be called upon. And Mrs Dove loved her daughter once more and wished she had the tongue to tell her so, and Alice the ear to listen. She crept back into bed and waited for the morning tea that the brochure had promised her.

When Alice awoke, she realised that she had slept peacefully the whole night. She felt very ashamed. She had no right to the sleep of the just and the innocent, and she was glad when she felt a soreness in her body, looking upon it as proper punishment. As the cabin door opened to the tinkling of cups, she hid her head under the blankets fearful of the tray-bearer. But she heard a woman's voice as the tray settled by her bed, and she uncovered her face, smiling.

She saw Ellen stir herself awake and she prepared herself for a recital of her evening's deck-promenade.

'We had a lovely walk,' Ellen said, even as she lifted her head from the pillow, as if all the words she had meant to spill, on her return to the cabin, she had kept in her cheated mouth the whole night. 'You should have come,' she added.

Ellen didn't know how right she was, but never, Alice swore to herself, never would she know the reason.

'He's a real gentleman,' Ellen prattled on. Alice wondered what was the difference between a real gentleman and a gentleman pure and simple.

'He didn't say or do anything improper,' Ellen added offering her own definition of what in her mind was a gentleman authentic. Which positively ruled out Alice's nocturnal companion, but for some reason she felt her stained and verbally assaulted self far superior to the untouched righteous Ellen.

'Surely you didn't expect him to do anything, did you?' she asked.

'You know men,' Ellen said, as if after a lifetime of nymphomania, 'they're all the same.'

Alice thought that was rubbish. Mr Bowers was very

different from her night-caller, and Pickering was nothing like either of them. She wondered who Ellen had in mind in making her blanket judgement, whether Walsh or Thomas, or both. For a moment she was tempted to divulge her secret, simply to give Ellen some sense of perspective, but she decided against it. The benefit to Ellen might be too costly to herself.

'I found a comb on my bed last night,' Ellen said suddenly. 'A man's comb. you didn't have a vistor, Alice, did you?' Ellen roared with laughter at the sheer impossibility of such an event. Alice coloured and hoped that Ellen would take it as a flush, though in any other circumstances, such an interpretation would have been deeply offensive.

'A steward came to turn down the beds,' she squeaked. 'He must have dropped it. I was in the bathroom,' she added quickly, declaring her innocence in the matter of the comb and any other concern that Ellen might have in mind.

'It smells of brilliantine,' Ellen said. 'Thomas used to use it,' she added with a certain nostalgia.

Alice smiled to herself. She considered that now she knew everything there was to be known about Thomas. The brilliantine told it all.

'Where did you put it?' she said.

'It's on the dressing-table.'

Alice had an urge to reach for it, to sniff it out, and she was horrified that after all her rage of the previous night, after all her shame, her appetite still lingered.

'You can give it back to him tonight,' Ellen was saying.

'Where will *you* be?' Alice asked, frightened.

'I shall probably be walking the deck with Mr Bowers,' she said. 'He suggested it.'

'Could I...' Alice started.

'Yes, of course,' Ellen said. 'A turn about the deck is very refreshing after dinner.'

The mention of dinner startled Alice once more. How could she face him, or he, her, for that matter? Would he serve the chocolate mousse as if nothing had happened? She wondered whether it would be against the rules to change their table. But they would have to ask Mr Bowers permission for that, and perhaps he might be offended.

'I'm looking forward to breakfast,' Ellen was saying,

sipping her tea. 'I never eat it at home, but somehow it's different when you're away.'

Oh my God, Alice thought. She'd only connected her caller with dinner, but there was no reason why he shouldn't wait at breakfast too. She would brazen it out, she decided. She would stare at him, and if he dared smile at her, she would turn her head with disdain. She felt in a fighting mood, anxious now to reach the dining-room and put him squarely in his menial place. As she rose from the bed, she gave a squeak of pain. Her body ached with an unaccustomed discomfort, unlocatable.

'What's the matter?' Ellen said.

'Just a crick in my back,' Alice improvised.

'It's age,' Ellen said.

It's youth, Alice thought, but she let Ellen's diagnosis lie. 'I'll lie in a hot bath,' she said. 'I won't be long.'

She hobbled to the bathroom, passing the comb on the way. She wondered whether he had used it before entering the cabin. She hoped so. She hoped he'd wanted to look his best, though she suspected that he had felt no need to present himself in a respectable light, since the last thing he had in his mind was any form of courtship. In the bathroom she undressed, avoiding any sight of her body, and wallowed in the heat of the water until the soreness subsided, while Ellen sat at the dressing-table sniffing at the memory of poor Thomas, and regretting that Mr Bowers did not put brilliantine on his hair.

When they reached the dining-room, Alice stood aside to let Ellen go first. She was suddenly afraid. She dogged Ellen's shadow as they crossed the floor, making for the table where Mr Bowers was already seated.

'Good morning, ladies,' he said. 'Did you sleep well?'

'Yes,' Alice said quickly, then regretted that her response was so swift, cutting the air with pre-emptive denial. Mr Bowers quite positively raised his eyebrow, but allowed that as his only comment.

'No-one said you didn't,' Ellen said, who rarely refrained from comment and certainly not when silence would have been preferable. Alice felt suddenly very tearful, and would have returned straightway to her room, had she not feared a bed-maker's presence. For she had not seen him in the dining-room, or any waiter for that matter.

'No service for breakfast, it seems,' Mr Bowers was saying. 'It seems we have to help ourselves. The buffet's in the smaller dining-room. I was waiting for you in case we missed each other.'

'That's very kind of you,' Ellen said, and he took her arm, reaching out for Alice on the other side, and led them into the dining annexe. From the archway, Alice could see a long buffet table, and a row of waiters serving behind. She panicked.

'I just want coffee,' she said quickly. 'Could you get me a cup, Ellen?'

'What's the matter?' Ellen said. 'I know you always eat a big breakfast. Must have something in your stomach to start off the day,' she said.

'Must fortify oneself,' Mr Bowers added, as if they were on route to some perilous adventure. Which indeed they were in Alice's mind, though only she knew of the danger ahead.

Mr Bowers pulled persuasively on her arm, so that she was obliged to follow him, and so solicitous was he, that he guided her in front of him, so that poor Alice found herself first in line at the buffet table. There were few other guests, and most of them were collecting their coffees at the end of the table. Alice scanned the row of waiters, but not their faces. She kept her eyes firmly on their waists, so that at least on her part there would be no recognition. If he was there, and he wanted to look at her, it was up to him to accommodate the consequences. For herself, she could not afford them. She took a plate and walked slowly along the table, taking small portions of her favourite breakfast foods. Mr Bowers and Ellen did likewise behind her, and all was managed in silence. She neared the coffee section.

'Black or white, Madam?' she heard, and she smelled the brilliantine. She knew that she wanted white, and she tried to say so, but no word would come from her. Her lips seemed suddenly too feeble to form any articulate sound, save that of a sigh of deeply remembered joy that his smell had rekindled throughout her body. She was trembling. She raised her eyes and looked at him with a look of love that was unmistakeable. She pointed to the milk, not trusting her voice. He poured it. She noticed that his hand was firm. She examined each bone from wrist to knuckle, for the first time in her life aware of its

45

contours. This is how a man is made, she thought. This is how he is joined and welded into an instrument of love. She wanted to know that hand, but she knew too, that in their kind of congress, the hand played a small if any role at all. She was tempted to touch it. Instead she stared at him, and he at her, but fleetingly, with no flicker of recognition, no token of guilt, shame, regret or renewed appetite. She gaped at him.

'Black or white?' he was asking Mr Bowers.

Alice shivered her way to an empty table, the tray rattling in her hands. She sat down. She didn't know why his indifference had offended her. Had he smiled or given her any form of recognition, she would have felt equally insulted. But there was something threatening about his indifference. It questioned her memory. She could not dismiss from her mind the nagging proposition that all that had happened in her cabin the night before was a figment of her imagination. Then with joy she remembered the comb, as positive proof that he had at least been there. But it proved no more, she had to admit to herself. Only his presence. There was no proof of his singing syllables in her ear, of his raging rhythms or of the small earthquake in her startled womb. His body on hers had left no prints, any more than the bird in the air or the lizard on the grass. But what proof could there ever be, she thought, even if he came again, and again and again? What proof of coupling, even in licit love save that of a witness or consequent harvest, both of which for Alice were beyond the bounds of possibility. She wondered how people could tell whether or not they were mad, how the limits of sanity were known, or the fitful frontiers of fantasy. And she wondered, too, why such thoughts had never before in her life assailed her. She thought of Pickering and his love-making, though that was a word she would never have used in his time. She tried to think of him tenderly. He had, all his life, been gentle, loyal and honest. Now she knew that she had discovered something to blame him for, and therefore something to forgive. For he had not sparked her. In all their nights he had given her no hunger. He had given her no thirst. In his simple decent way, he had given her his love, but in no way had he disturbed her. How else could one fly into fantasy but on the wings of disturbance, on the propulsion of hunger and need? For the forty-odd years of her marriage, she had been grounded. She had done her duty by him as her mother had told her, or rather taught her without words, as she herself did her duty by her father. Now Alice understood the possible cost one paid for fantasy, and not only did she forgive Pickering, but she blessed him.

'Are you alright?' she heard Ellen say, and looked up as Mr Bowers put down his tray and Ellen's on the table. 'You're looking deathly pale.'

'Yes,' Alice said, and meant it. For some reason, she suddenly felt much better. She was glad the waiter had shown no signs of recognition. He couldn't, for he, no doubt, had it in mind to come to her again.

They were at a trestle table, designed for random seating, and soon they were joined by a couple who, despite the empty spaces along each side, placed themselves next to Alice.

'I'm Betty Knox,' the woman said as she sat down, 'and this is my husband, Jack. Say hello Jack,' she said like a ventriloquist talking to his doll.

'Hello,' her husband Jack said dutifully but without a smile, for that had not been part of his wife's request. He's doing his duty by her, Alice thought, as his father had wordlessly taught him, and she tried to picture the two of them in their nights together, and she horrified herself with such an alien thought.

Mr Bowers felt that the woman's introduction deserved some feedback, for courtesy's sake, and he stood, and introduced himself and his companions. And with this he would have been happy to conclude the exchange, but their uninvited proximity seemed to require at least some trivia of conversation. Alice searched in her mind for something to say, but Ellen didn't bother. She felt she could safely leave it in Mr Bowers' capable hands.

'Is this your first cruise?' he said, and Ellen and Alice marvelled at his conversational gifts.

'No, we've...' Jack started, then he quickly recovered himself, and in response to a life-time's obedience, he said, 'You tell them Betty.'

Betty paused, not for any dramatic effect, but in acknowledgement to her husband that he knew his place. Alice began to dislike her. They were about the same age, and

Pickering would have been Jack's, had he lived. She felt a greater affinity with Jack because, in her terms, Betty was behaving like a man.

'This is our fourth cruise,' Betty was saying. 'We just love the sea, don't we, Jack?'

And Jack nodded, whether he liked it or not, for she had told him to.

'Mind you, I wouldn't go on a long trip,' she was saying, 'one that went on for weeks without stopping. Have to stretch your legs from time to time on dry land. Isn't that right, Jack?'

'If you say so,' Jack dared.

Betty looked at him, sniffing the onset of rebellion. And Ellen leaned forward, and even the good Mr Bowers, silently rooting for good old Jack.

'Don't you like dry land?' Ellen ventured, stirring it a little. And then, playing his card, Mr Bowers said, 'Men are natural sea-going creatures.'

A great smile suffused Mr Knox's face. A man had accepted him as one of his gender. It gave him courage. 'Women always like to play safe,' he said. He was shouting a little, like a coward turned bully while his own back was turned. 'A man doesn't talk so much, but it's he who takes the risks.'

Mr Bowers thought that Jack had perhaps overstepped his licence, and he regretted his initial encouragement. Even Ellen and Alice, though much on Jack's side, feared the consequences of his sudden rebellion. But Jack, sniffing a small victory, and with allies by his side, was not going to forego what he considered an advantage. Had he taken the trouble to look at his wife's face, he would have known better than to exploit his assumed ascendancy, knowing perhaps that that look was a weapon no arms of his could counter. 'Women talk a lot,' he shouted. 'They make a lot of noise,' he was practically screaming now, 'but it's the man who quietly gets on with the job.' He paused, panting, hearing the echo of his words, and suddenly terrified by their dark reverberations. That surely must be his trump, Alice thought, and she pitied him for his poor hand. Mr Bowers looked at Mrs Knox's face, and its slow gathering of blood-red rage, and he hoped to God that Jack would say no more.

'Where would men be without women though?' Ellen said suddenly. She wasn't exactly changing sides, but she sensed something of a personal attack in Jack's trump card. And Alice, more in support of Ellen than in defence of the strength of her sex, said, 'If it's the men getting on with the job, they're not doing so marvellously what with wars and everything.' She astonished herself, and the smile that Ellen flashed her, she found faintly insulting. She would never have talked like that to Pickering.

'We all need each other,' Mr Bowers said, a peace-maker. 'Man cannot live without woman, or vice versa.'

But it seemed that Betty Knox could, if not without all men, then at least without her present incumbent. As she opened her mouth to counter-attack, she simultaneously rose from her seat, and her audience waited for the clap of thunder. Mr Knox shrank in his chair, quailing.

But God is occasionally good. For a split second He forsook His priorities to widows and orphans and gave His full undivided attention to the Colonised Man. For the expected clap of thunder came not out of Betty Knox's mouth, but somewhere from their starboard, as a great wave lashed the bows of the ship which heaved with a sudden and startled effrontery. Mr Knox was too overcome with gratitude for his God-given acquittal to notice the sudden pallor on his wife's face. He did not know that all the red vocabulary that had gathered in her mouth now curdled with the rising bile of nausea. She rose unsteadily, needy for air, but unable to articulate her need, for an open mouth could not be trusted to sieve the words and the words alone. Then Mr Knox dared to look at her. He knew he should rise and take her arm, but he was fearful of a public dismissal. He had, after all, behaved very badly. Mr Bowers refrained from rising, unwilling to usurp Jack Knox's marital duties. But Jack remained seated, dealing with his guilt, and so did Mr Bowers, concerned with his decorum.

Betty Knox weaved her way alone to the door of the dining-annexe, but fell flat on her face before making it.

And still the men sat, their guilt and decorum now compounded. Ellen and Alice ran towards her, and the waiters too, and Alice suddenly thrilled to a saviour's role that she could now share with her own glorious redeemer. She was ashamed of such a thought but relished it nonetheless. They formed a circle round Betty's prone body like some ritual girdle around a sacrifice. There was blood too, a trickle on the neck, and something other than blood which spelt itself out in letters larger than any sacrifice. A large brown ring spread and continued to spread over the centre of Betty Knox's white linen skirt, widening its muddy circle under their eyes. Blood, as long as there was life, was replaceable, feeding like lactation, on its own loss. But this emission would not renew itself. It was waste, unrecyclable; it was shame, irrefutable; it was gross nakedness beyond any hope of cover. It was a sacrifice far more impertinent than blood, and as the brown ring widened, they stood, transfixed by its threat, and Ellen and Alice moved towards each other, as if in apology for their frail gender. For had it been a man lying there, his trousers spattered with his waste, it would have aroused not mockery, not ridicule, but a mutual understanding of their own kind, for on a man, the brown ring would have been a mark of blatant manhood and a wise acknowledgement of a natural function, while on a white linen skirt, it spelt weakness and stupidity.

The sea was suddenly calm, and there now seemed no reason why a body should be lying on the floor unless it were for sleep, or for that unthinkable coda mutely orchestrated to the brown trickle between poor Betty's legs. Jack Knox trembled. It was he who had spread her there; his rebellious words had laid her low. 'Oh God,' he whispered, 'don't let her die.' Not now, at least. Later perhaps, but not now, at this moment, when the blame could be laid so squarely at his door.

Mr Bowers stepped forward and it was a signal to the waiters to make a move. Jack Knox couldn't stir, though he knew it was his place, his duty, his business and his alone to gauge the extent of his trespass and to face it like a man. Whatever that meant. Alice and Ellen, though guiltless, were immoveable too. It had now become Man's work, a task of responsibility and knowledge, to turn Betty over and see what should be done. Alice watched them, as Mr Bowers clasped her shoulders and the other men her feet, and turned her over as they might a roast in the oven. In her fall she had split her chin, and a trickle of blood ran down her neck onto her white blouse. Her eyes were closed, but her mouth was open and askew, to accommodate her upper denture which was dislodged in her fall. Alice looked at Ellen and was ashamed. They hoped that poor Betty would never know. Neither need she, for it was information that had no visible proof, and could be kept from her for ever. Unlike the brown stain of her skirt, for which she would have to find some rationale, and neither Ellen nor Alice could think of a possible explanation other than that which it truly was. Poor Betty when she came to. Which she was at this moment doing, while the good Mr Bowers was attempting to re-fix the denture on her upper jaw. He managed it, taking his hands away as Betty opened her eyes. A waiter bent down and put some water to her lips and Alice saw that Betty's saviour was her own, and a small ripple of jealousy stole through her. How gentle he was, his hand cupping the back of her head, his soothing words in her ear. Alice turned away.

'You're alright now,' she heard Mr Bowers say. 'Would you like to try and stand?'

Then she turned and saw how he lifted Betty to her feet, with her saviour on the other side.

'Oh my blouse,' Betty said, noting the blood stains on the front. The waiters grinned. Poor Betty had not yet seen the back of her skirt. Jack could remain on the side-lines no longer. Now that he was mercifully exonerated, he went willingly to her side. He put his arm about her waist, his jacket hanging loosely from his finger to shield the skirt's shame. 'I'll take her to our cabin,' he said.

'I'll send the doctor to look at that chin,' a waiter said, not Alice's, but another, but his tone of concern rang as sweetly in Alice's ear. She day-dreamed that if ever sea-sickness overcame her, it would be within his waiting station, and she could faint into his arms. She shivered. I must get rid of these fantasies, she told herself. They are not good for me. Yet they were pleasurable. After a lifetime of indifference to men, of fear and timidity in their presence, she now found that she loved each single one of them, and would have bedded them all. She shuddered, while Arthur Pickering, astonished and multi-cuckold, turned over in his grave.

A number of passengers had collected at the door of the dining-annexe, held there by a steward until the drama was played out. Amongst them, Mrs Dove and Alice, who had both returned to sleep after their morning tea. On waking again, they had exchanged a few syllables. Alice had declared she was hungry, and Mrs Dove admitted that she was looking forward to her bacon and egg. It was no earth-shattering exchange, but it was a beginning. When Alice dressed, donning her denim dungarees, the habitual silence once again held sway. Mrs Dove knew better now than to make any comment. Their conversation, such as it was, was confined to very simple remarks that could mean nothing else but simply what they actually said. No sub-titling, no projection. They reached the dining-room in time to join the line of passengers waiting for entry after the Knox's curtain. Now they shuffled inside, picking at the crumbs of the crisis, pointing to the table where Betty Knox had taken her meal, the path she had trod to her hoped-for deliverance, the exact location of her fall. Betty Knox had become almost a celebrity. Her name would be dropped on many an evening in countless drawing-rooms over the years, along with holiday stories and snapshots. And when the men were alone, they would snicker at mention of Betty Knox's not-so-white skirt.

Mrs Dove was happy to note the buffet arrangements and the consequent freedom to choose one's own seating. They collected their breakfast trays, and because Alice was first in line, it was up to Mrs Dove to follow her, and hope that she would opt for company. But Alice skirted the multi-populated central table and made for a single near the wall. It was conspicuously isolated, and Mrs Dove was irritated that she had been led into such solitude. And apprehensive too. For a crowded table would have obviated conversation between them, whereas alone, against the wall, their mutual silence was on public display. Or perhaps Alice wanted to be alone exactly for privacy's sake, in order to make some attempt at communication, and this prospect unnerved Mrs Dove even more than the silence. She took her seat, and did not look at her daughter, but concentrated her gaze on her egg and bacon breakfast. For the first time, she noted the tasteful combination of food-colours and their varying textures. She stared into her plate, on the perilous verge of daydream, and was startled by the sudden greeting at her side. She looked up. It was Mr Bowers, with his two ladies yoked to his side.

'Good morning to you both,' he said cheerfully. 'I hope you passed a peaceful night.'

Mrs Dove looked up at him, astonished. It was her first extra-mural communication of the cruise. She wanted to ask them to sit down, but the table Alice had chosen could accommodate no more than the two of them, and once again she tried not to hate Alice for her meanness of spirit.

'Very well, thank you,' she said.

'We shall see you on the deck no doubt,' Mr Bowers said. He was clearly about to leave, and Mrs Dove had no excuse to detain him.

'Yes,' she said timidly. 'After our breakfast.'

'I'm going to write some letters,' her daughter said, losing no time in excluding herself from the party promenade.

'Then perhaps we shall see you, Mrs ... er...,' Mr Bowers invited.

'Mrs Dove,' she said. 'Stella Dove.' She did not introduce her daughter for fear of what hostility she would show, and she knew well her fulsome talent in that direction.

'I'm Mr Bowers,' he said, smiling, 'Victor Bowers, and this is Mrs Walsh and Mrs Pickering.'

Ellen and Alice smiled, sorry for her, pitying her loneliness which was so apparent from the hostile presence at her side.

'We'll see you on deck,' Ellen said, pulling on Mr Bowers' arm.

And they were suddenly gone and Mrs Dove knew that she could not join them after breakfast because she was too timid to do it alone. She tried not to catch Alice's eye, and concentrated on her now tepid egg and bacon for which she had lost all appetite.

'I'm going to the writing-room,' Alice said suddenly.

'Oh wait for me,' Mrs Dove pleaded. 'Wait till I've finished my coffee.'

Alice drummed her fingers on the table. I should never have come, she thought to herself. And her mother gulped her coffee knowing that it had been a terrible mistake to invite her. They rose from the table together, and Mrs Dove, fearful of being seen alone, hurried back to her cabin. She sat on her bed and wondered how she would weather the next three weeks. She wished she were at home. Her living-room, her kitchen, her bedroom, her garden, each space was cluttered with aids to postponement. There were a thousand things to do to delay confrontation. But here, in the cabin, there was nothing familiar, no object of safety, no landing-strip of comfort, no sign-posts to her past and the few memories that were consoling. There were so many things she wanted to know about her Alice and in this bare cabin, unarmed, exposed, the questions were screaming aloud. They were shaping themselves on her lips, beyond her control. She heard them, trying not to listen. Why had Alice been deserted by Richard, that oh so kind gentleman who had given her everything, who was chivalry itself? She knew that her Alice had wanted to continue with her teaching, but surely that was little enough to give up in return for the comforts he was giving her. He had rights after all. His lavish housekeeping allowance entitled him to his pleasures. He was a man after all, and men were different. Mrs Dove just couldn't understand it.

Then there was Nellie. What on earth was Nellie, with her one-roomed flat and its single bed? And where on earth was her little Alice sleeping? Mrs Dove shut her eyes in horror at this gate-crashing thought. Oh God, she whispered, whatever is to become of her?

And the same thought was passing through Alice's mind as she sat in the writing-room with the ship's writing-paper in front of her, staring at the three loaded words that had shot from her pen. *My darlingest Nellie.* She was sure of none of them. Not even the name. Once she had looked inside Nellie's passport, but the face that she knew so well was named Beatrice. She was afraid to ask Nellie about the deception because it might have led to a quarrel. The 'darlingest' was a formality, a word that Nellie would have expected, and the 'my' was obligatory. Nellie would have insisted on that. But Alice did not feel the words as her own. It was as if Nellie had dictated them, ordering Alice's love-object and granting full possession. But Alice did not love Nellie. She was simply moved by her. By those great unwatered eyes of hers, by her raging rigid body, stiff still from her father's rape. She was moved by Nellie's need, her hunger, her craving, longing. But she did not love her. Not if that was the same word she would have used for Richard. In Nellie's arms, she thought only of Richard, despite all the hurt he had caused her. When he had left her, there had seemed much reason in his departure, though it had amazed her. For a whole month she had hopped from one anonymous bachelor-bed to another, on a rampage of coital punishment. And as her rage subsided, so did her man-appetite, until finally it soured altogether. This she knew to be her greatest loss, a loss she mourned on each awakening.

She'd met Nellie at a women's meeting. A friend of Richard's had taken her there. The speaker on the platform had spelt out for Alice all her questionings, had validated all her complaints. Nellie was kind and sympathetic at first. Compassion was part of her wooing-technique, and carried about her person as separately as a handkerchief. Over the weeks of her involvement with the women's movement, it had seemed to Alice to be undeniably logical to move in with Nellie. A relationship with a woman had become a political necessity. But her heart was never in it. Gradually, that which she gave to Nellie, she was giving out of pity, and Nellie's hold on her was exactly that blackmail. Alice stared at the three intimidating words on the paper, Nellie's voices exacting their tribute, and she crunched the paper under her hand. She tried not to think of what would become of her.

She left the writing-room and went on deck, almost colliding with Mr Bowers and his ladies.

'We are keeping an eye out for your mother,' Mr Bowers said.

'I'm looking for her myself,' Alice lied, and quickly left them as if for a search.

'An unhappy girl,' Mr Bowers declared. 'We must befriend her. Her mother too, is distressed. There is so much unhappiness,' he added, almost to himself.

'Like the Knoxes,' Ellen said, and Alice was irritated by the reference. She had hoped that they wouldn't talk about Mrs Knox, as if any reference to that subject was but a veiled discussion of women in general, so she was annoyed when Ellen said, 'Poor woman,' as if in invitation to a re-play of the drama. Alice felt it treacherous. In many ways, Betty Knox had got what was coming to her, but she'd been unable to control her punishment, and such injustice was far beyond the merits of her crime. We women should stick together, Alice thought, and wondered why Ellen didn't think likewise, since it was she who was always going on about liberation.

'I hate to see an unhappy marriage,' Mr Bowers said.

'I don't think it's all that unhappy,' Ellen said. She herself had bossed poor old Walsh about in her time, and would have done the same for Thomas had he survived their hedge. 'She's got into the habit of nagging, and he's become used to being nagged. They probably couldn't manage any other way. Not any more. It's a habit.'

'I wonder what they're doing now,' Alice said.

'Well I wouldn't like to be in his shoes,' Mrs Bowers said. 'Not once she's up and about. He's probably on his knees with apology.'

Mr Bowers was wrong. The apologies had been made and accepted. Whatever had led Betty Knox to this present state had lime-lighted her, had called doctors and stewards to attendance, and a publicly devoted husband at her side. Moreover, she was now well, and could be up and about on doctor's orders, and the incident should be forgotten. When they'd reached their cabin, Betty had stroked Jack's hand. 'You're going to have to put up with me for a little longer,' she said smiling. 'Were there many people in the dining-room when it happened?' she asked.

Gently he responded to her need of audience. 'It was crowded,' he said. Almost all the passengers were having breakfast at the same time.'

Betty Knox smiled. She wanted to rise from her bed and go out and greet them all as a survivor, to receive their best wishes and smiles and deference. 'I'll take a shower,' she said, 'and change my clothes.'

It was then that Jack Knox began to tremble. For though he had nothing to do with the white linen skirt, it was he who would pay for its staining and her explosive shame. He watched her into the bathroom and waited for the shit to hit the fan. He did not have to wait long. 'Jack,' she screamed after a few seconds. She managed to endow his name with trisyllability.

'What's the matter?' he said, though he knew full well the cause, but any words, however meaningless, would serve to pass the time and perhaps blunt the edge of her explosion.

56

'*How* many people were in the dining-room?' she yelled through the bathroom door.

Now he regretted having fed her stardom. A full house, then, could not, in such short retrospect, be emptied. Now at this moment, the truth would sing, and more than sing, as it would have jarred in her moment of limelight.

She opened the bathroom door, and stood naked and raging in the threshold. He dared not look at her.

'How many people?' she yelled at him again, as if he were responsible for the gate.

'It was pretty full,' he said to his corner, 'but most of them were on the other side.'

It made no sense to him nor to her, and his well-meant attempt to placate her only served to enrage her further.

'And the waiters? Where were they?' she said.

'They were serving.'

'You're a liar,' she screamed at him. 'They were all looking after me. I saw them.'

He couldn't deny it. He went over to her and put his hand on her shoulder. 'It's nothing to be ashamed of,' he said. 'It could have happened to anybody.'

'But it happened to *me*,' she said. 'I'm not anybody.' The aura of stardom was not so quickly dispersed. She took his hand from her shoulder. 'We're leaving,' she said. 'We'll get off at Bordeaux. Pack the cases.'

He stared at her. 'But we've only just started,' he said.

'We're docking this afternoon and we're getting off.' She'd opened the wardrobe and was flinging her clothes onto the bed.

'We won't get our money back,' he tried, as a last appeal to her sense of economy.

'My pride is worth more,' she said, 'and if you had any respect for me, you'd understand. You'd be the first to take me off this boat and away from all the shame.'

'I was enjoying it,' he said feebly. 'The cruise, I mean. We don't have to go,' he shouted. 'In a few days it will all be forgotten.'

'You do what you like,' she said, with time-honoured confidence that he would dumbly follow her. 'I'm leaving at Bordeaux.'

'And I'm staying,' he said, knowing that this verbal

declaration of his independence was all that he could manage, and that in the afternoon, he would follow her off the ship like the lackey he had been for so many years.

'I'm staying,' he shouted, the battle already lost.

For answer she unzipped his suitcase and threw it on the bed. He hated her. He tried one last time. 'Please change your mind,' he begged. 'Once we're home, you'll regret it.'

'You'll regret it too,' she said.

'It wasn't my fault,' Jack Knox almost whimpered.

'No?' She paused in her packing. 'You and your talk about men being important, and women just chatterers. Insulting me publicly in front of those women, and that … that fairy.' She spat out the word. It was a term Betty Knox used for any man she could not conquer or comprehend.

'It was the wave,' Jack Knox said. 'You fainted because of the wave.'

But nothing untoward had ever happened in Betty Knox's life either by natural or even divine intervention. There always had to be somebody to blame and, in her married years, it had usually been her husband. It was his fault that she had no children, though she had been declared sterile by a panel of doctors, that same panel that had confirmed Jack's fertility. But the doctors were male, all of them, and had ganged together to defend one of their kind. Even Betty Knox could have qualified for a conscience-raising women's group at times. Though she disliked women almost as much as men, she could, if it was convenient, subscribe to their struggle.

'It had nothing to do with the wave,' she shouted. 'I fainted because you insulted me.'

She stormed into the bathroom and returned with his sponge-bag, which she flung into his case.

'I'm not going,' he said, but with little assurance, like a child whimpering his rebellion yet clinging to his mother's hand.

'If you think I'm handing over the money,' she said, 'you're mistaken. I'm taking the plane home, and I shall need it all.'

He knew he was powerless. He looked at his open sponge-bag lying in his case. He saw the tail of his tooth-brush, the tuft of his shaving-stick, the screw-cap of his liver-pills, the black teeth of his comb. Yet even in these highly personal accoutrements, concerning *his* body, *his* well-being, *his* public survival, even in these he sensed no possession. They were hers, all of them, her allowances to him, her permit to his cleanliness, her licence to his liver.

'Now start packing,' she was saying.

It was not even an order. It was permission granted, with the implication that it would be for his own good. He was almost weeping in acknowledgement of his own frailty. He looked up at her with abject loathing. He bitterly regretted that she hadn't expired on that floor, the brown stain on her skirt as her final signature. He would have learned to live with the guilt, which in time he could lay at her own door. Thus her death would have been self-merited, and his own reward. Now she stood before him, full of the miserable years to come, and, knowing that the battle, even if one could dignify it by that name, was now utterly lost, and that he would dog her angry footsteps back to their miserable semi-detached, now that there was no chance of reconsideration, he blew. And blew mightily.

'Your teeth fell out too,' he shouted at her. He was almost screaming with malicious joy. 'That man with those women, he put them back in your mouth. Everybody was looking.' He burst breathless into peals of laughter. 'You looked terrible,' he said, doubled up with the glee of it, and his wife's curdling humiliation.

Betty fingered her teeth. She did not believe him. She dared not believe him. Even in leaving the ship that afternoon, she would have to accommodate the stares and whispers along the halls, the decks, the gangways to the waterfront. The brown stain on her skirt would provoke titters perhaps, but in the main they would be murmurs of pity, for that end of her was not her deliberate doing. No blame could be attached to that involuntary gesture, that was only a natural and universal accompaniment to an unconscious state. But her teeth were another matter. They, and the fact of their mobility was of her own doing, her own fault, her self-neglect in her childhood, her lack of self-esteem. They were against nature and, as such, an object of shame. She turned her back on him and took them out, examining them for cracks or mis-alignment. Her dentist had promised her they could never be detected, leave alone dislodged, except by her own doing. She would kill him when she got home. But he was not to hand, and her anger was extreme. But Jack was there, and he would do, as he would always do as a sieve for her spleen. She replaced her teeth and like a blazing dragon, turned on him. 'Go to the purser and cancel our reservations,' she said. She thrust the tickets into his hand. He took them meekly. Jack Knox made small demands on life and, in his narrow vision, he considered themselves quits. He went to the door. 'I'll do your packing,' she said, and as he went out, he actually thanked her.

When they landed near Bordeaux, the Knoxes waited in their cabins, as the passengers temporarily disembarked. Jack was appointed sentry, as a look-out, and when all was clear, he took the cases and nodded to his wife to follow him. For once, she hovered in his shadow, her head lowered, her ears alert for any alien footfall. They reached the gangway to the waterfront. 'It's only the natives now,' Jack said, and he quickened his step, and she, hers, he humping the cases, and she with her hand on his shoulder, like two thieves making a successful getaway. Except for one witness.

The waiter stood on the topmost deck, taking the air and formulating his plans. He smiled to himself. He watched the wretched couple as they crossed the quay-side, the woman's head still bowed, then onto the square and the row of taxis. He watched them settle themselves into the first car, and followed them until they were out of sight. Then he turned, smiling, and made his way to the purser's cabin.

Towards evening, the passengers filtered back onto the ship and made for their cabins to dress for dinner. The waiter, in his quarters, greased his hair, and again missed his comb. Now, with his newly planned proposition, was a good time to retrieve it. He made his way to the ladies' cabin, and knocked discreetly on their door.

Inside, Alice was painting her finger-nails, while Ellen was combing her hair. When they heard the knock on the door, Alice started. Her hand slipped and smudged her finger with red paint. She knew who it was, and rose to go to the bathroom to hide herself from a possible confrontation. But Ellen, whose conscience, such as it was, was virgin clear, had already said 'Come in,' and he was in the room, his smell preceding him, with Alice standing, her fingers bloodied, trembling like a fern. He was staring at her. She prayed that he would not approach her. What there was between them, and that she could not define, nor would she try for fear her conclusions would force her to end it, but whatever it was, it required no witness, and she looked at him, shaking her head, and at the same time indicating, with her bloodied finger, Ellen's presence at the dressing table. He winked, understanding. Then she realised what she'd done. Not only had she sanctioned their former congress, but she had invited a further instalment. His wink was an acknowledgement of that. She had in all ways colluded, and she feared both for her life and for the excitement that that fear engendered. She sat down knowing that escape was by now superfluous.

'Did I by any chance leave my comb here?' he said. 'I'm checking on all the cabins. Perhaps it fell out of my pocket when I was turning down the beds.' He knew it was in no other cabin. He had left it in this one deliberately, as a thief might leave his print to add excitement to the risk of discovery.

'We thought it was yours,' Ellen said, picking it off the dressing-table, and sniffing at poor Thomas as she handed it over. She would have liked to have kept it a while. He took it, used it once through his hair, and pocketed it. 'The Knoxes have left the ship,' he said, and the women wondered at its relevance.

'Poor Mrs Knox,' Ellen said, for she felt that some response was called for, though she couldn't help thinking it was not a waiter's business to indulge in passenger gossip.

'Their room is free,' he said.

It was Alice who first understood its relevance, and she shuddered.

'You could have it, if you want,' he went on, addressing his remark to the innocent Ellen. 'It wouldn't cost you anything extra. The purser suggested it,' he added quickly, putting himself in the clear. 'Might as well have a private room each,' he said.

'Oh that would be lovely,' Ellen said without looking at her friend for consultation. It did not occur to her that Alice could possibly object to such a privilege. 'A private room each,' she said, turning to Alice. 'What a stroke of luck. Though I'm sorry about Mrs Knox,' she added, without any sorrow.

'Then if you'd like to pack your bags,' he said to her, 'I'll move them during dinner. It's cabin 47E.'

He was gone before she could enter into discussion with her friend, and possibly be persuaded to change her mind. His smell lingered on the closed door, and Alice turned her head away, sniffing. 'Are you sure you want to be on your own, Ellen?' she said, without looking at her.

'Why not? It'll be fun. I can visit you, and you can visit me. To think of it, a private room each. It would have cost us a fortune.'

'Won't you be lonely?' Alice tried again.

Ellen heard her fear. 'I won't go if you don't want me to,' she said. 'But what's there to be afraid of?'

'Nothing,' Alice said quickly. And everything, she thought, for his way was now clear and at any time.

Ellen pulled her suitcase from under the bed. Alice was dismayed. Short of tears, there was no way she could keep Ellen as a safeguard. She watched her as she folded her underwear neatly into her case. 'I won't pack my dresses,' she said. 'He can carry them on the hangers.' As the wardrobe and drawers emptied, Alice felt more and more vulnerable, more and more unarmed. The space left by each dress was a chink in what frail armour she possessed, the emptying shoe-rack, and the denuded dressing-table, a fissure in her poor citadel. She was powerless to intervene.

'I'll be ready soon,' Ellen said, 'and you haven't finished with your nails.'

Alice looked at her bloodied fingers. She thought she might leave them untouched. They would be apt ornament for her nocturnal role, for she was convinced of his coming.

'You can't go into the dining-room with nails like that,' Ellen said. 'What would Mr Bowers think?'

Alice didn't very much care what he thought, and she wondered why Ellen was so concerned on his behalf. 'D'you fancy Mr Bowers?' Alice dared to ask.

Ellen laughed, rather too shrilly, Alice thought. 'He's not my type,' Ellen said, and Alice thought that only people like Ellen could have a 'type,' because she was so experienced. She wondered what her own type was, and whether it was Pickering. Her small experience gave her no means of measurement. She dared to think of her night-caller. Was *he* her type? He had nothing in common with Pickering, yet she had served them both. She preferred to think that it was Pickering who was her sort of man. It seemed to make her more respectable. 'What's your type, Ellen?' she asked, as she wiped the polish from her finger. 'Walsh of course,' Ellen said, because she had to. To have spent most of her life with a man not to her taste was an admission of marriage failure. But in her heart Ellen knew that Thomas was closer to her kind, and that Mr Bowers was light years away from either of them. Yet with a little encouragement on his part, Ellen was more than prepared to tailor her type. 'No,' she said again. 'Mr Bowers is nothing like Walsh. What's your type, Alice?' Ellen said.

'Pickering,' she said, then added, 'I suppose, but he's the only man I've ever known.' She was lying to her best friend and she felt a thrill in the deception. She finished painting her nails. She would never have considered such an adornment in Pickering's time. Painted nails were whore's equipment, and not in his house, never, he had once shouted, when Alice had innocently tried it out. 'Throw that stuff away,' he'd raised his voice to her, fearful of what unknown factor would upset their harmony. For he'd seen it as a threat, that red paint, and known it for its evil, by the the unaccustomed thrill in his loins. But Alice hadn't thrown it away. She'd buried it in her handkerchief drawer, and forgotten it. But when she was packing for the cruise, she'd rediscovered it, and tried it out, and smelt the tingly risk in it. She'd turned her head away, and slipped it into her sponge-bag, sensing that whatever harmony she had achieved since Pickering's passing, now stood in some need of disturbance. Ellen had always painted her nails, even when Walsh was alive, and Alice wondered what flagrant form of discord Ellen had invented to disturb her widowhood.

'Are we ready?' Ellen said.

Alice blew on her nails. She picked up her evening bag and went to the door. For the first time she noticed that it had a chain attached, like the one on her own front door at home, which was only used when Pickering was no more. The chain on this door did not please her. Its presence gave her choice, licensed her to the fulfillment of her desire or its deliberate disallowance. She didn't want to have to choose. If he came it had to be his responsibility, and her receiving of him was her helplessness. That way, her image was more respectable.

They made their way to the dining-room.

They were surprised to find their table unoccupied. Mr Bowers was always so punctual. They sat down and hoped the waiter would delay service until Mr Bowers arrived. Alice looked around the dining-room. She did not expect to see her caller, whom she presumed was, at this very moment, clearing her cabin of any impediment to his return visit. She shivered at the thought. Then she caught sight of Mr Bowers, and looked again to ascertain whether it was indeed their supposed cruise-companion. On a second glance there was no doubt about it. It was their Mr Bowers alright, and ensconced, very cosily it seemed, with that Mrs Dove who was alone at her table. Alice was relieved to note that they were not eating. It was possible that Mr Bowers had passed by and had paused for brief conversation while awaiting his regular ladies. Even so, Alice was nervous of pointing him out to Ellen who had begun to regard Mr Bowers as her exclusive property. But Ellen had caught sight of him too.

'Well, you could knock me over,' she said to Alice, and Alice thought Ellen was over-reacting a little. Mr Bowers had every right to talk to anybody he pleased.

'He's not eating with her, Ellen,' she said, offering a crumb of comfort. 'He'll come over in a while.'

'Well I'm not waiting,' Ellen sulked and she looked around for service.

'Let's wait a little,' Alice said. 'He's only chatting.'

Which in truth was exactly what Mr Bowers was doing. He had passed Mrs Dove's table on his way to his own, and found her sitting there forlorn and alone. To have passed her by would have looked like deliberate avoidance, and his courtesy had prompted his stopover.

'Where is your daughter tonight, Mrs Dove?' he'd asked. 'Not indisposed, I hope.'

Mrs Dove was overwhelmingly grateful for his memory of her name and, by way of reward, she offered him her daughter's seat. But first she looked round at his regular table to make sure that his ladies had not yet arrived. She did not want to be seen to be poaching. But since they were not in sight, she felt free to offer him her poor company.

'My daughter isn't hungry,' she said. 'She won't be taking dinner.'

It was on the tip of Mr Bowers' tongue to invite her to his regular table, but he was unsure of the welcome that Ellen and Alice would afford her. Besides it would look particularly greedy on his part to collect what would appear to be the beginnings of a harem. And in time there would be her daughter too, that strange unhappy creature, ill-fitting in any company. So instead, he said, 'We missed you on deck this morning.'

'I had letters to write,' Mrs Dove improvised. She couldn't confess that timidity had kept her to her cabin.

'Tomorrow morning, perhaps?' Mr Bowers said.

'If ... if I have time,' she parried. She knew that in the morning her timidity would be no less.

'What are you so busy doing?' Mr Bowers asked. 'I don't mean to seem inquisitive,' he added quickly, 'but you are, after all, on holiday.'

Mrs Dove smiled, and Mr Bowers thought he saw her eyes mist over, but when he looked again, the eyes were clear. He felt deeply sorry for her.

He looked round at his table and saw that his ladies had arrived. He noted that Ellen looked very cross and that Alice was trying to pacify her. He had no doubt that it was on his account. But despite the tension that clearly simmered at that table, he was determined not to leave Mrs Dove on her own. It would seem an act of sheer rudeness not to invite her to join them.

'Won't you dine with us, Mrs Dove?' he said. 'It's silly for you to sit here on your own.'

Her eyes shone with such intense thankfulness that it made him uneasy. 'Please come. We would enjoy your company,' he said, each syllable against his better judgement.

'I'd be delighted,' she said, and started to rise, trembling with gratitude. Then he noted a cloud shadow her face. Over Mr Bowers' shoulder, she had caught sight of her daughter entering the dining-room. Alice had decided she was hungry after all. She had not even bothered to change her dungarees.

'Here's my daughter after all,' Mrs Dove whispered, as if spreading rumour of impending calamity. Mr Bowers turned and saw her, and wondered why she hadn't changed for dinner. It was grossly ill-mannered, he thought. 'Oh that's nice for you, Mrs Dove,' he said, though it was quite clear to both of them that Alice's arrival could bring pleasure to nobody. 'Now you won't be alone,' he said. And he left her with unaccustomed haste and made for the safety of his own table.

Mrs Dove lowered herself once more into her seat and could not look at her daughter who had, yet again, thwarted her pleasure.

'I don't mind if you sit with them,' Alice said. 'I'm quite happy to be on my own.' And though Mrs Dove would have welcomed some untrammelled company, she couldn't publicly leave her daughter on her own, for fear it might look like a family quarrel.

'No, I'm happy to sit with you,' she lied. But she knew, too, that to sit with others and to view her daughter's isolation would have been far more painful. She smiled into her empty plate, and hoped that Alice would see it, and know that, though mis-addressed, it was meant for her. And, picking it up, Alice felt a sudden surge of pity for her mother and she too smiled into her unopened napkin on the table.

At Mr Bowers' table, apologies had been offered and accepted. Ellen was so glad to have Mr Bowers safely at her side, that she was quick to forgive his temporary philandering.

'You don't have to apologise,' she was saying, with the security of one in possession. 'You can talk to anyone you please.'

Whatever did Ellen see in him, Alice wondered. She examined him closely for the first time. Although his reliable presence was a comfort, a security, she did not find him attractive. In fact, his very decency and politeness irritated her, since it underlined her own lack of self-esteem. Ellen, on the other hand, was much taken by his courtesy, or so it seemed, as if she accepted it as her due, and found no reason to be obliged to it, or to pay for it in any way. But Alice needed desperately to be *grateful,* and for each bowing and scraping of Mr Bowers' feet, she felt the need to offer him at least her body, if not her spirit. She had the impression that men were not interested in the spirit, anyhow. But he could have had her body, and she would have considered even that a small recompense. She envied Ellen who seemed untouched by any sense of obligation.

'There's a dance after dinner,' Mr Bowers said excitedly as he drew out their chairs.

'I can't dance,' Alice said quickly, to pre-empt any embarrassment on Mr Bowers' behalf. For it was clear in Alice's mind that Mr Bowers would partner Ellen, and would only out of gentlemanly duties guide Alice onto the floor.

'It's a long time since I've danced,' Ellen said, a remark which declared her dancing ability, but at the same time excused her possible awkwardness. Mr Bowers would make allowances for that.

'I'm a bit rusty too,' he said, 'though I do like a turn on the floor.'

Alice looked around the dining-room, but could see no sign of her suitor. He was probably still humping Ellen's bags. She hoped he might have dropped his comb on her bed as signal to a later call. A turned-down visiting card. His aroma for starters. She shivered and remembered the inconvenient chain on the door. It signified her control, her authority. It forced her to decide between what she wanted or did not want. Alice had never been schooled in decision-making, and all the small ills that had befallen her in her life she had happily ascribed to that ignorance.

A waiter, a stranger, approached their table, and announced that tonight the Dover sole was to be strongly recommended. And Ellen and Alice, through want of glasses, agreed that that would be their choice, and Mr Bowers, shoving his above his forehead, examined the menu and decided on a simple steak and salad. 'That gives us a wine problem,' he said when the waiter had gone away.

Neither Ellen nor Alice understood the nature of the problem, but both suspected it was a financial one. Ellen's appetite for Mr Bowers soured a little and Alice was not in the least bit surprised because she always said that nothing was for nothing.

'Oh we'll buy this one,' Ellen said quickly, sharing Alice's disgusted glance.

'Oh it's not that,' Mr Bowers said. 'Forgive me ladies, but it's my pleasure to buy the wine. It's simply a question of whether we should have red or white.'

Even so, Alice didn't see it as a problem, and if Mr Bowers

was paying, she felt it was her unspoken duty, and Ellen's, to settle for whatever colour he wanted.

'I *should* have red,' he was saying, as if it was against the law to have otherwise, 'and you ladies, with your fish, should have white.'

'Oh we'll have red,' said Alice. 'We don't mind.'

'I think we'll have a half carafe of each,' he said, and Ellen thought him most accommodating, and began to fancy him again, but by the same token, his continued accommodation was beginning to get on Alice's nerves, and she hungered for the brutal indifference of her night-caller.

Mr Bowers signalled to the wine-waiter and the divided order was dispatched.

'I've had a bit of luck,' Ellen said, when their meal was set before them.

'Luck?' Mr Bowers said.

'Yes. I've been given my own private cabin. The Knoxes have left the ship, you know.'

'Ah, it's an ill wind,' Mr Bowers said. 'You will feel quite luxurious. Both of you, privately ensconced.'

Alice did not know what he meant, but she was unnerved by the salivation on his lips as he said it. She liked Mr Bowers less and less, so she had to remind herself of his wine-bill to keep her equilibrium. 'Tell us about your wife, Mr Bowers,' she suddenly said. She knew it was rather forward of her, but she sensed she had to divert that salivation into a channel that was assumedly more respectable. Ellen looked at her askance. But Alice could have been forgiven for trying. She was not to know that Mr Bowers' salivation was but the expression of his enjoyment in his each and every syllable. For that was all the enjoyment he was capable of. His vocabulary, and it was not mean, was his suitor's apparel, his articulation, his gilt-edged calling card, and his style, his proposal. Each consonant was a rose, each labial a token of his love. His gallantry was his foreplay, his courtesy, his coupling. He had a million pistols, but all, alas, unloaded.

'She was a beautiful woman,' he said, 'given much to kindness and sympathy. I was lucky. I shall not meet her kind again. In many ways she was nonpareil.' Alice and Ellen let that word hover. Whatever it meant, it sounded complimentary and called for a pause to savour its echo.

68

'We were lucky too, weren't we Alice?' Ellen said after a while, meaning that whatever it was that that word meant, it could apply to her Walsh too, and even perhaps to Thomas, though she suspected that, disparate as they were, they could not have had even a word in common.

'Then we are all very fortunate,' Mr Bowers said. 'We have all been granted a beautiful memory. Let's drink to that,' he said, raising his glass, and now Alice liked him a little better, because on one level at least, though she knew it was not justified, he had accepted her as equal.

The waiter brought round the sweet trolley. Mr Bowers declined. He said he was sated, and wished to preserve what energy he had in spinning his ladies around the dance floor. Alice was giddied by the mere suggestion, and was straightway put off the charlotte russe that she had intended. Instead she settled for a mild and inoffensive sorbet, while Ellen, less giddied, dared the strawberry flan.

Some of the diners were already making their way to the ballroom, and the slow, quick quick, slow rhythms of a foxtrot could be heard from a distant band. Its tempo gave Alice confidence, and Ellen too, for it was the same that had scored their girlhood across parquet dance halls in spotlit City Halls. Alice recalled her first dancing dress, a pink thoroughly net affair that her mother had made, and for which fitting she'd had to stand on the dining-room table to gauge an equal length all round. *The Nature-lovers' Ball*, it had said on the ticket, that her mother got free because she was on the committee, so Alice went partnerless and terrified. Walter Biggs – Alice flushed as the name startled her tongue – whose mother was also a committee member, was bludgeoned into attendance by a similar complimentary, and on the basis of this fragile common denominator, their respective mothers considered that their children were made for each other. Alice's interest in things of nature was very marginal, and Walter Biggs even less, though he did not admit to it and, hanging onto her waist on the dancing-floor, his sweaty fingers wandering, he claimed a legitimate curiosity in all things natural. Alice smiled at the recollection.

'Are we fit and ready to perform?' Mr Bowers said, when they had finished their dessert. Ellen felt like a young girl and she giggled behind her handkerchief. Alice had an anxious moment considering how Mr Bowers would divide his dancing attentions. She found herself hoping that he would favour Ellen because she could not cope with Ellen's jealousy.

On their way out of the dining-room, Ellen was careful to steer Mr Bowers away from the Dove table. She feared he would invite them to the ball. But Mr Bowers needed no encouragement from Ellen. He wove his way through the centre of the diners, his eyes fixed firmly on the floor. Mrs Dove watched his departure with a deep sense of loss. She wouldn't have gone to the ball even if he'd asked her. But he might have given her the opportunity to decline his offer. Unlike Ellen and Alice who, in their moments of stress, gave automatic thought to their hedge-cutters, the spirit of the late William Dove lay undisturbed, never to be called upon. As a source of comfort or security, he was as unreliable in death as he was in life itself. While he lived, she sought refuge in her garden, so as she watched Mr Bowers' hurried exit, she wished herself among her tulips, her secateurs in her hand.

The ball-room was dimly lit. A large multi-coloured crystal ball hung from the centre of the ceiling and spun slowly, shedding a faltering rainbow on the dancers below. A seven-piece band was assembled on the dais, white evening-suited, with a violinist who doubled as conductor. A young singer, poured from a diamanté mould, proclaimed with all her teenage years that when she was too old to dream, she'd have her love to remember. Which seemed a pretty pointed lyric to let loose among the ageing cautious limbs on the floor.

Mr Bowers guided his ladies to the gilt chairs that ringed the room. He stood in front of them bowing. 'Now, which one of you will honour me?' he said.

Ellen thought him a coward, his leaving the decision to them, but Alice thought it was a gallant move, obviating offence to either of them.

'You go, Ellen,' Alice said. 'I'll watch you.'

Ellen needed little prompting. She rose and wriggled her body into a posture of presentation. Mr Bowers put his arm loosely about her waist and guided her in a waltzing rhythm onto the floor. 'So kiss me my sweet, and so let us part,' the diamanté urged from the platform, and Alice blushed vicariously and kept her eyes on her lap in her embarrass-ment. And very soon she saw a pair of black-trousered legs saunter past her, and pause, and she heard a voice, which from its proximity must have belonged to the legs, that requested the pleasure of her partnership. She thought she recognised the voice, but there was no smell in it, and she was disappointed, for her night-caller might well have been on the dance floor as illegitimately as he was on any part of the ship. She raised her eyes, and saw a portly gentleman, slightly stooped, with a thatch of hair so thick and so black that it was unquestionably against nature. Alice was flustered. She did not trust her dancing foot-steps, but she was dying to try them out, and she knew that Ellen would feel much happier if she were not lining the wall shrieking her friend's responsibility. She smiled. 'I'm a little out of practice,' she said. 'And I'm very patient,' he answered. He handed her his arm. For a moment she listened to the music, and watched the rainbow of light as it stroked her dress. She took her suitor's arm and she knew that this moment of her life was, beyond any doubt, a moment of high romance, such as she had read so often in the mild-chocolate-stained novels on her bedside table. He led her onto the floor.

'My name's Wallace,' he said. 'My friends call me Wally.'

'My name's Alice,' she said. 'Alice Pickering.'

He now felt it in order to put his hand on her waist and propel her into the stream of waltzers. He held her at some distance from his body, and further than was necessary to accommodate his paunch. At first, Alice was grateful for the space between, but then, as they passed Ellen and Mr Bowers, she regretted the lack of public intimacy. Nonetheless, she called out to Ellen and smiled. Look at me Ellen, she meant to say, somebody wants me.

Ellen was pleased with the thought that she might now have Mr Bowers all to herself for the evening and, with luck, if Alice's partner retained his interest, for the duration of the cruise. She felt so light-hearted and happy that she missed her beat, lapsing contrary to all rhythms into a foxtrot, and Mr Bowers gently diverted her, as if she was going through the wrong door.

The band was working itself up into a crescendo and the singer assured the dancers, for what, by her shrilling voice, threatened to be the last time, that when they were too old to dream, they would have a night like this to remember. Alice

71

began to have fears that her partner might be disappointed in her and refrain from a second invitation. But even as the drummer raised his stick for the final roll, Wally was asking for more, and Alice tried not to feel so desperately grateful. She felt happy too, and she murmured apologies to Pickering, assuring him that the happiness he had given her was of quite a different quality, though she couldn't specify in which way. But it was a happiness she would never seek or find in anybody else. Of that she was confidentially sure, for both Wally and her night-caller spoke a very different language.

Wally guided her to the gilt chairs, and they were soon joined by Ellen and Mr Bowers. Alice effected the introductions, and Ellen was confident of a foursome. They sat for a while, discreetly regaining their breath, and all around the circumference of gilt chairs, there was much panting and heavy breathing, mostly behind the hand, or otherwise disguised, for it was not a young gathering, yet it had the vanity of youth. Some of the gentlemen dispersed to get their partners drinks, and Mr Bowers and Wally took their cue, and returned shortly afterwards with glasses of lemonade. They had little breath left for conversation, so they sipped politely and smiled at each other. After a while the master of ceremonies announced that the next turn on the floor would be a spot dance, and carefully he outlined the rules. From time to time, the music would stop, and those found dancing outside the spot-light's arc would be eliminated. Until only one couple remained and that couple would win a prize. The master of ceremonies nodded to the band leader who raised his violin bow. The band started on a medley from *My Fair Lady* and the couples rose. Slowly the ballroom lights dimmed into almost total darkness, and, after a second, a spotlight from the ceiling described an arc of light on the centre of the floor. Mindful of the rules, the couples rushed into the arc, their haste impeded by their paired years, hogging the light, dancing on the spot as it were, for fear of elimination.

'Keep moving,' the master of ceremonies shouted, 'keep moving around the floor.'

And so they did with obedience, for despite their years, with their bows and their flounces, they were children again, and the master of ceremonies, alone and in authority, held paternal sway. The music went on and on, and allowed them in time to reach the arc of light again and pray that the music would stop in their illumination. And as the music got into its stride, swelling its theme, and seeming to deny interruption, it suddenly stopped and so did the dancers on their cue. Those couples marginally outside the spotlight edged their way into its reflection. Some were caught by the watchful master of ceremonies, and were dishonourably discharged from the floor, and they walked away giggling to hide their shame. Alice and Wally were squarely in the light's circle, and so was Ellen, though Mr Bowers' bottom was dangerously on the fringe, but he edged it in quickly, with little movement, and managed to get away with it. The band started up again, and almost immediately stopped. Ellen and Alice, who'd hardly got into their steps, were again survivors, though many couples, who with confidence had darted outside the ring of light, were caught in the shadows and dismissed. The band struck up again. Now the couples on the floor were countable. The failures on the gilt-chair fringe disappeared for lemonade, unable in their childish years to bear the victory of others for, once off the floor, they were old again, the appetite of youth curdled by the bitterness of their calendar. The diamanté vocalist joined the band at this juncture, shrilling that she could have danced all night, a capability far beyond those who still survived on the floor. But they shuffled along, nervous of the shadows, and the failure that lurked in the dark. When the music stopped, only three couples were caught in the arc's light. Alice and Wally were amongst them. Alice was fearful of catching Ellen's eye, but Wally was waving his hands across the room, guiltless of his survival. Alice turned to watch Ellen as she and Mr Bowers were leaving the floor. She smiled wanly, and Ellen had the decency to mouth, 'Good luck,' as she faded away into the shadows.

There was a long pause before the music started up again. The tension was almost unbearable, and Alice wished that it was she and not Ellen who'd been eliminated. She saw Ellen on the sidelines and noticed that her arm was in Mr Bowers'. She was glad for her. It would compensate for her failure. Yet she envied her. She didn't want to be a runner-up. She wished she could go for lemonade like the others. Above all she wished that she would not win, for she could not accommodate the embarrassment of success.

The band struck up with a drum roll to signal the last instalment of the game. 'Now spread out,' the master of ceremonies ordered. And they did, each one of them, on the outer ring of the bull's eye. They danced as the band went on interminably and Alice relaxed a little. But Wally was pulling her to the centre again. She felt an anger in his grip, and the petulance of a bad loser. She began to dislike him a little. Yet she was too timid to pull away and she followed where he led. She noticed that he took longer strides, that he swung her in an ever-widening circle, so that when the crunch came, he covered his ground to the bull's eye. She felt ashamed of his greed, and hoped that in the other dancers' eyes it would not reflect on herself. Wally was pirouetting in the very eye of the beam when the music cut out, and there was no doubt as to the winner. The two other couples gracefully withdrew, applauding the winners as they went. And the applause was taken up by the other losers who now gathered around the gilt chairs. Wally stood transfixed in the spot-light, as the master of ceremonies approached them, bearing two gift-wrapped prizes. Alice dared to look at Ellen. Her arm was still mercifully locked to Mr Bowers', so Alice forgave her for not joining in the applause. Ellen wished her well, however, with her one unoccupied arm, by waving it frantically in a congratulatory gesture. Mr Bowers did likewise on the other side. They were like two amputees with a mutual and gratefully accepted handicap.

'What are your names?' the master of ceremonies asked them.

Alice hesitated before identifying herself. She was always conscious of what the neighbours would say, even on an ocean-going liner. But Wally had no such scruples.

'This is Alice,' he said. 'And I'm Wally.' He felt that, in the cruise atmosphere of strict bonhomie, the surnames would not be necessary.

The master of ceremonies did not probe further. He signalled for a drum-roll and as its echo rumbled, he shouted, 'The winners are AliceandWally.' He elided their names, coupling them. Wally took Alice's arm and actually kissed her, full on the lips, when she wasn't looking. It was as if he needed publicly to confirm the coupling that the master of ceremonies had hinted at in his announcement. Alice felt her eyes water. She had a blinding flash of recall of her last kiss. And behind it was the solid, reliable, respectable and oh so painfully decent mouth of Pickering.

He had come into their bedroom, tear-stained from his mother's funeral. She herself had been unable to go because of a broken ankle which was in a plaster-cast, and fairly immobilised her. Pickering had loved his mother with simple and guiltless affection. He would not mourn her long for guilt would not prolong his grief; he would simply miss her with an enduring sadness. Alice recalled his trembling lower lip as he came towards the bed. He'd sat by her side, leaned over, and without touching her with any part of him, he'd sealed her lips with his. Not hard, not deep, but with a strength born of his terrible pain. It was a kiss without lust, and with no hint of foreplay. It was his declaration to himself that he was still amongst the living and, to her, that she was by his side.

Alice looked at Wally and gave him a public smile, but she knew she wanted to spend no more time with him. The master of ceremonies handed over the gifts while the band told them they were jolly good fellows. And as the other dancers were drawn to the centre of attraction, clapping and singing as they approached, it seemed incumbent on Alice that her gift should be opened. Wally had already torn off his wrapping and tried to hide his disappointment at the sight of a bottle of after-shave lotion. He had hoped for more for his pains. Then he started to tear at Alice's wrapping to see if she had fared any better.

'Mind the ribbon,' Alice said quietly. She wanted it for Ellen as a gift in consolation. Wally handed over the ribbon with disdain, and rummaged at the packaging. Inside was a box, and, with an alien shred of courtesy, Wally handed it over for Alice's opening. Inside was a bottle of perfume which proclaimed with its brand, *I'm Yours*. Alice quickly put her finger over the label. Whoever the aroma might be for, it was certainly not for Wally. She knew without doubt, and with a small thrill of shame, the natural recipient of any product that declared her unabashed and total availability. She would exchange her aroma for his brilliantine. She could hardly wait for night to fall.

They renewed their foursome. Ellen was still soldered to Mr Bowers in an armlock that had become quite unnerving, and Alice wondered how, and more important when, the two of them would cut adrift. Wally, seeing their token of togetherness, attempted to duplicate it with Alice, but Alice slung her hand behind her back and drew away, because she did not wish him to touch any part of her. When the band struck up again, she claimed fatigue and made her way to the gilt chairs, hoping that Wally would not follow her. She sat down and waited for what she assumed was his inevitable approach. She dared not look in his direction, out of two distinctly opposed fears, one that he was on his way to her and the other that he had disappeared. After a while, she dared to look up at the dance-floor. She saw his trousers first, the baggy black bags with his paunch overflowing the waist band. His arms were in possession of an endless waist that sub-divided a woman rather taller than himself who was viewing his thatched hair with some disdain. Wally had quickly found other fish to fry, and Alice's relief was spiced with anger and jealousy. She caught Ellen's eye as she skirted the floor, and was ashamed to look at her. I've failed again, Ellen, she thought, and hoped she would forgive her. Ellen pretended she hadn't seen her, and she steered Mr Bowers away from Alice's line of vision.

For herself, Alice didn't in the least mind being a wallflower. She had a rendezvous to look forward to, and a gift-token to pay for it. She wished the band would play *God save the Queen*, when they could all, in all decency and without humiliation, take themselves to bed. Then, as if to oblige, the master of ceremonies' voice broke through the decrescendo of the band and announced that this would be the last dance. At that moment, Mr Bowers caught sight of Alice's wallflower status, and he guided Ellen to the fringe of the floor. He bowed to Alice's gilt chair. 'May I have the pleasure of you both?' he said. Alice looked timidly at Ellen for her sharing permission, for it was clear in Alice's mind where Mr Bowers' affections lay. Ellen was gracious and urged her to join them. Mr Bowers gave them each an arm and circled them onto the floor. Fortunately it was a waltz, a tempo more conducive to threesome than any other and, seeing their formation, couples separated and joined with others until the dancers were a

76

large laughing circle. The master of ceremonies was delighted and thought that he was a very good organiser indeed. The circle had created a space for the descent of his balloons, and they showered down, lit by the swirling rainbow, to the delight of the passengers who thought they'd entered fairy-land. There was no scramble to collect them, for it was clear there were enough for everybody, though Alice did catch sight of Wally who was making an undignified dash into the balloon shower. Then a drum-roll called them all to atten-tion, a reminder that the fun and games were over, that they must wipe their tired feet, and mind their manners for homage to the Queen. Mr Bowers stood very erect, in a posture throbbing with responsibility and respect, an attitude he maintained until the anthem was over. Then the drums rolled again, and the passengers, ballon-laden, dispersed.

Mr Bowers suggested a turn around the deck, and perhaps a night-cap before they turned in. Alice excused herself, pleading fatigue. There was no point now in waiting for Ellen. She was to be alone anyway. She walked with them as far as the deck, and, saying goodnight, she handed over her package ribbon to Ellen. 'That's for your hankies,' she said.

The radiant smile on Ellen's face showed she was in little need of consolation, and Alice suspected that, during the course of the evening, Mr Bowers and her friend had established a little more than mere connection. She was happy for her. After all, she had her own mystery, less tangible perhaps, and certainly carrying a greater risk. She almost ran to her cabin, but on approaching the door, she grew suddenly afraid, with a startled awareness of the madness she was courting. She wished now she'd taken a turn on the deck, and delayed whatever adventure awaited her. She turned the door-handle slowly and quietly, half expecting to find him there, and not wishing to disturb. But the door opened onto an empty cabin, and yawning spaces in the open wardrobe, and one single unsheeted bed, all spelling out the terror of Ellen's absence. As she closed the door, her hand brushed against the chain, and reminded her that there was choice. She sidled it into the lock and at once felt safe. But as she undressed, she recalled his hot syllables in her ear, and she thought of Ellen arm-locked to Mr Bowers, and her self-righteous need to protect herself began to bore her.

She slipped the chain-lock out of its catch and, panting, got into bed.

She listened for his footfall. After a while, she heard steps. Her body tightened with fear. She stared, petrified, at the chain on her door, hanging loose with invitation. The steps resounded closer. There was now no time to get to the chain and save herself. She thought of Pickering and had a sudden and frightening assurance that she would soon join him. The steps approached the door, as her heart faltered. Then they passed and faded down the corridor. She uttered a small prayer for her deliverance, then sidled out of bed and put the chain in its catch.

But she needn't have bothered. The waiter had already dropped his comb on Ellen's bed.

CHAPTER FIVE

Another change of quarters

He knew her name from a perusal of the passenger list, but names were of minor importance to him. He would never employ a name in his operations. Their use would have been an unnatural intrusion into a procedure which flourished on its basic anonymity. The use of a name, whatever it was, would have translated into a relationship that which was purely and simply a connection. The waiter was interested in nothing more than that. So though he knew her as Ellen, in his mind, she was the 'other' one, the difficult one, as opposed to her companion whom he knew from long experience would be a push-over. So he had prepared himself for Ellen and all the resistance he had expected of her.

While she was still on deck taking the air, which he had ascertained from his own look-out, he had sauntered to cabin 47E and prepared for her return. In his inside pocket he carried a silent polaroid camera and a screwdriver. Once inside the cabin, he quickly unscrewed the chain-lock from the door. In his experience, chains were the most serious impediment to entry and he wished to save himself future trouble. Having de-fortressed the door, he set his camera and hid himself behind the cupboard opposite the dressing-table. He waited. He knew he would not have to wait for long. From his perusal of Mr Bowers' belongings in his cabin, he knew that he was not a night-bird; from his regular diary, he'd learned that he was stable and not given to permissiveness of any kind. Other things too he had learned, but they were not for the telling. At least, not until they might come in handy for possible blackmail. On Mr Bower's bedside-table was an ivory-bound Bible, and this spoke to the waiter of his nightly faith. Even Mr Bowers' shoes and clothes were so educated that they denied any moral illiteracy. The waiter

79

prided himself on his understanding of character. It was a highly useful talent in his line of business.

After a while, he heard the cabin door-handle turn, and he relaxed his body so that it would make no sound. From the chink behind the cupboard, wide enough for the camera eye, he watched Ellen's movements as she prepared for bed. He noticed that she was smiling, no doubt with Bowers-recollection and aftertaste. She glowed as if a goodnight kiss still hovered about her mouth, though the waiter doubted it, recalling Bowers' Bible at his bedside. She was giggling with joy and he actually heard a small gurgle from her throat. She began to undress. He'd taken a chance on her nudity in the bedroom. The odds were slim that it would pay off. In his experience it was rare that a single woman unclothed herself in front of herself, in a space with mirrors, where that self, usually embarrassed and ashamed, would be multiplied. But this one, in her present joy, could clearly bear to look at herself, and even to pause a while, and to admire each part without the need of a gown or night-dress to camouflage her age or inadequacy. At last she was fully naked. She turned to view herself in the full-length mirror on the wardrobe door. She was smiling still, as if she were actually posing for him. He couldn't have wished for a better light, a better composition, or a greater co-operation. The finished picture would be more than a piece of blackmail. It would be a work of art. The thought crossed his mind that he might enter it for a photographic competition.

He pressed the button on her smiling full frontal, and waited. After a few seconds the proof slid noiselessly out of the mouth of the machine. He waited, letting it lie there, for his later perusal and admiration. Ellen picked up her nightie from the bed and went into the bathroom. It was in this interval that he crept out of his hiding-place and silently reached the cabin door. Once outside, he waited, then walked down the corridor to the broom cupboard. Inside, he tore off the photograph, examined it, and found it hugely to his satisfaction. She had posed for him, and for him alone. No observer could have denied it. He left his camera on the cupboard shelf, slipped the photograph into his inside pocket and went about his bed-making business.

He stopped at her door and listened. He heard her singing.

'I could have danced all night,' she trilled, and the uneven unsteady timbre of her voice was a reliable barometer of her age. He put it in the mid-sixties and he was satisfied. He knocked gently on her door.

'Come in,' he heard. There was an excited expectation in her voice, and he knew that his non-Bowers face would be a disappointment. But he was prepared for that, and he arranged an innocent smile. He opened the door, and wove his grin around it. 'May I prepare the bed?' he said.

She was shocked that this stranger had discovered her so expectant. The smile dissolved from her face and she nodded her permission, wondering why he had left his duties so late. As he bent down to turn the blanket, his comb fell onto the bed. His perfumed calling-card. He pocketed it and its perfume lingered on the counterpane. Ellen walked over to the bed and took off her slippers. As she was bending down, her back to him, he took her gently by the shoulders and drew her towards him. Then he turned her, and laid her on the bed. He noticed that one slipper was still attached, and this he removed, then laid her flat on her back and took a moment to look at her. Ellen's eyes were wide open, and in some bewilderment, for she had not yet understood what was happening to her. And as she saw the face above her, the grin widening, she suddenly fathomed the terrifying implications of her position. She opened her mouth to scream. But he was ready for her, having timed it to the second, and he put his hand over her mouth, and felt her startled saliva trickle down his palm. She was certainly not Alice, he thought. She was the 'other one'.

'Now don't make a sound,' he said, 'and you'll come to no harm.'

Her eyes widened with her fear, and he tightened his grip on her mouth.

'Not a sound, d'you understand?'

She nodded furiously, wanting above all her life, her continuity, her morrow for Mr Bowers and all the morrows that he would greet her.

The waiter took his hand away. This is rape, she thought, a word she had read from time to time in heated headlines. She saw the pictures that those headlines captioned, and they were bed-sprawled, bloody and lately dead.

'Don't kill me,' she whispered. 'Please.'

He smiled. 'You just lie there,' he said, 'until I'm finished.'

Finished what, she thought, though she knew and dared not think of it. She heard the movement of a zip and gave an infinitely sad thought to her buttoned Walsh. Buttons had no part in rape; zip was its signature tune, its tempo, its rage. He lay gently on top of her, but his weight was leaden. She heard her heart raging. Her fear for survival was primary, so that his rough jabbing, his humming and the filth he was pouring in her ear, were of secondary concern, for she knew that once they were over, and he gone from the cabin, the fear would remain. She would not die of his assault, or of his songs or of his words; she would die simply of the fear itself. She felt the sweat trickling down her hair-line, and her ears damp with tears. And then a great rage flooded her, and plans for report, for revenge, for immediate trial and retribution. With these thoughts she tried to comfort herself. From his rhythms she knew it must soon be over, and she began to look forward to the revenge she would wreak on him. As soon as he was gone, she would dress, just her dressing-gown would do, screaming all the time for attention. She would make her way to the purser's office crying for help. Someone must hear her, someone must follow her pointed finger and track him down. Someone must bring her to him where he was lying trapped, where she would crush him like a worm, over and over again, until he was a red pulp on the floor, and still she would crush him, through hair, flesh and bone. She was panting with her imagined exertions, her frenzy exhausted her.

He rose, patted her legs together and said, 'How old are you?' And she, though mindful of her flirtation with notions of women's liberation, though still reeking with the assault, though chockfull of revenge, hesitated. For stronger than all of these was her vanity. 'Forty-five,' she dared.

He smiled. 'I'll be going,' he said.

She heard the zip again, and waited, fearful, for his receding footsteps.

But he stood there, watching her. Again she feared for her life, and as he put his hand in the inside pocket of his jacket, she thought for certain that her end had come. She closed her eyes and prayed.

'Sit up,' he said, and, though his voice was gentle, there

was no question of its tone of order. She raised herself slowly. He held the photograph in front of her. She squinted.

'D'you need your glasses?' he said. He was anxious to accommodate her. She nodded and pointed to the dressing-table. He reached for them and handed them to her. She put them on.

'Now look at it closely,' he said.

She put out her hand to hold it. 'Don't touch it,' he shouted at her. 'Just look at it. Look at it carefully.'

And she did. With horror. 'It's not true,' she said.

'Don't you remember posing for me?' He smiled. 'Taking off all your clothes and posing for me? Especially for me?' he added.

Ellen was not slow to get the message. Now she knew that any idea of revenge was no longer plausible. And as if to re-inforce her conclusion, he said, 'So you don't need to be getting any ideas about reporting me. I came to your cabin simply to turn down your bed. You asked me to stay. You wanted me to take your photograph. You posed for me.' He paused, then added, 'You smiled for me too.' He pocketed the photograph and walked towards the door. 'I'll be back,' he said. 'Tomorrow maybe. Maybe not. Perhaps the day after. Whenever I feel like it,' he said. The grin had faded from his face. He looked at Ellen with disgust. 'Sleep well,' he spat at her, and patting his breast pocket, he left the cabin.

She lay there shivering. She could not believe what had happened to her. She surely must have had a terrible dream. She sniffed the brilliantine and she gave a little cry. Was she dreaming the smell too? And the moist trickle between her thighs? She groaned. She had to get up and cleanse herself. She had to rinse the filth out of her; her purification would clear her mind and enable her to decide what she must do. As she undressed, she could not look at herself, and lying in the bath, she could not touch herself. She saw her body as so separate as to belong to somebody else and she loathed it for having been party to the assault. She clasped the taps, keeping her hands out of the water, trying to swirl her body so that it would be cleansed without her participation. She would sooner have bathed a leper than lay a single finger on herself. She began to cry as much for the assault as her inability to do anything about it. She knew that her only possible avenue of escape was a return to Alice. But she dare not give Alice the reason. She would never, never in her life tell anybody what had happened to her. She herself, when hearing of a rape story, had always harboured a sneaking suspicion that the victim had somehow asked for it, and she was not going to have Alice or anybody else impute such motives to herself. No, she must think of another reason for Alice's nightly company and protection. She would have to abase herself and plead loneliness. Alice would no doubt crow a little, and Ellen's pride would pay whatever price. But she must, on all accounts, get back to Alice's cabin. She looked at her watch. It was two-thirty. Alice would be asleep, and such was Ellen's plea that she could not risk her friend's irritation. She would have to sit it out till the morning. She would lock her cabin door and try to get some sleep. She shuffled towards the door, and she registered with terror the tell-tale print of the nut and bolt that had secured the chain on each side, and she knew that he himself had removed it, and his reason could only have been to facilitate his access at any time. She panicked again, and frantically looked around the cabin for any piece of furniture that was moveable. But all was fixed. Her suitcase, a frail canvas affair, was all she could pit against his entry. And this she shoved to the door. It would at least give her some notice of the next assault, though what she could do with the interval of warning she could not imagine. She could scream and cry out for help, but he would flash that damning photograph, irrefutable evidence that her cries, however piercing, were part and parcel of their lustful drama.

She sat on the edge of the Knox's bed. Exhausted as she was, she was loath to lie in it. The smell of his assault still wafted from the sheets. She would sit erect all night and count the hours to Alice's protection.

She set to wondering why he had singled her out. She did not associate rape with the notion of random. She had to feel there was something special about her that had attracted even such a monstrous villain. There were other women on the boat, mostly coupled, but one or two, she'd noticed at the tables, were alone, and easy bait for his filthy seduction. But, in her case, he had gone to the trouble of moving her quarters. It had to be because she was somewhat special to him, and this thought fed her vanity and eased her for a time.

But to be an object of such a rogue's devotion was in no way flattering, and this thought shamed her and curdled her rage once more. She looked at her watch. It was almost three o'clock. She thought she might go on deck for a while but she was frightened of meeting him, or any other night-bird who would suspect her wanderings. She was a prisoner, with freedom on neither side of the wall. She thought she might while away the time in rehearsal for her plea to Alice, but any preparation in that cause would only endow Alice with an importance and a power that Ellen was not willing to afford. Besides, she did not doubt for one moment that Alice would welcome her back. She had been loath to see her go in the first place. Indeed, Ellen's return could be construed by Alice as a favour, and Ellen would do nothing to disabuse her of that opinion. She managed to convince herself that a return to Alice's cabin was now only a matter of time. So, having settled that, she could afford to think of other things. And the idea of revenge, which had never entirely left her, now felt free to disport itself within the limitless bounds of her imagination. She was able for the moment to forget his damning photographic evidence, and she whiled the time away picking and choosing the tools of her attack, the instruments of his torture. From her memory of like circumstances in television or books, a woman's revenge smoked from a trembling pistol in a trembling hand, a hand that shook, not from cowardice, but from a nagging awareness, despite the righteousness of her cause, of the thirteenth commandment. Or perhaps the avenger would grasp a heavy object that was conveniently at hand and bring it down on the thick unsuspecting neck of her oppressor. But even then the hand would hover, mindful in its hesitation of a price that might have to be paid, either in this life or the hereafter. But a pistol was not for Ellen, she decided. It put too much distance between her and the object of her hate. Neither would she be satisfied with a heavy object raised on a turned back. In that action was too little premeditation, and she wanted her prior deliberation known, its timing, each stage of its growth, and every bloody thought that had nurtured it. And moreover she wanted him to witness it, his eyes fully open, liquid with his fear, and his mouth open to plead. And she would give him time, smiling all the while. And nothing about her would tremble. No thoughts of holy commandment would stay her hand, no sermon on the mount would disturb her, no God-bothering moment would in any way deter her from what she must do, and do gladly with lustful and remorseless appetite. As she sat on the edge of her bed, scheming her revenge, she trembled only with the sweet promise of its execution. But still she could think of no instrument that would satisfy her, that would fit snugly into her raging hand, that would amply translate her shuddering hatred of her attacker. And even if she decided on her exact instrument, how could she be sure of laying her hands on it? And what spot would she choose for his gallows?

With such thoughts, reality intruded upon her wild dreams and nudged her with a reminder of their fantasy. 'I'll kill him, I'll kill him,' she heard herself whisper. Everything was possible even if it first found root in the imagination. Where was love born if not in a daydream, and was not that love attainable? Hate was likewise nurtured in the mind and nourished there, and on the mind's shelf repeatedly rehearsed. Neither would it wane in the shadows. Hatred, like love, would not consume itself without public trial. She would not be hoodwinked into satisfaction by plain fantasy. No. She would kill him, by whatever means and in whatever place. Only then perhaps, she dared to hope, could she lay a finger on her own body.

For the rest of the night, Ellen sat on the edge of her bed, dwelling on her victim and herself as his executioner. And the more she dwelt on these thoughts, the more her appetite increased, and when she finally closed her eyes it was to succumb to sheer fatigue that even her frenzied thoughts of revenge could not conquer.

Alice was awoken the next morning by a rattling of the chain on her cabin door. On hearing it, she recalled her last night's rejection, and for a moment she thought it was he coming to claim his rights after an unavoidable delay.

'Who is it?' she called out, then regretted it, for his answer would give her the choice of barring or admitting him.

'It's Ellen,' she heard, and her friend's voice was a whisper as if she did not want her whereabouts known. Alice got quickly out of bed and unhooked the chain. Ellen crept inside, fingering the chain with satisfaction. It would increase her protection.

'What's the matter?' Alice said anxiously.

'Nothing,' Ellen said quickly. 'I woke up early and I thought ... well to tell you the truth, Alice, I got a bit lonely. You were right. I shouldn't have gone. So I'm bringing my things back here.'

Perhaps, if she had asked whether she could return, it would have been difficult for the timid Alice to deny her. But having taken Alice's acceptance so completely for granted, made Alice less timid, and she said, surprising herself with her firmness, 'No Ellen, I rather like having my own private room.'

Ellen was taken aback and she sat down to deal with her astonishment. She was angry. How dare Alice have such selfish thoughts, concerned only with her own comfort and convenience? She regretted that she had been so presumptuous in her decision to return. She should have asked for Alice's good favours. Now she would have to beg for them. 'But aren't you lonely too?' Ellen said, rather gruffly, in an attempt to postpone the plea that her pride would not allow.

'No,' Alice said, 'it's rather like being at home. Being alone is not the same as being lonely. Anyway, we're together all day, and will be for the next three weeks.' Alice was losing her confidence. She couldn't help feeling that she was being cruel to her friend and, having made a certain stand, she was now tempted to submit and to invite Ellen back to their common quarters.

'I think you're very inconsiderate,' Ellen said, and Alice no longer had difficulty in holding her ground. Ellen could be very mean sometimes. There was a silence between them. Short of a compromise, and it was not a situation that allowed for half measures, there was nothing more to say. Ellen eyed the chain on the door. 'This is a much nicer cabin than mine,' she said. 'It's more cosy.' She did not want Alice's company, she didn't even want the cosiness of her cabin, though in her present circumstances a change of address would have been highly desirable, she simply wanted Alice's door-chain and its clanging metal protection. Alice was glad of a loophole for gracious compromise. 'We'll swap then,' she said quickly. 'I'll take yours and you can come back here.'

Ellen tried to hide her delight. Logically an exchange of apartments was no cure for her alleged loneliness and she had to acknowledge that fact before accepting Alice's offer. 'It won't make any difference to being alone,' she said. 'But at least it will be familiar,' she added. Her one night's stay in Alice's cabin hardly allowed the familiarity she claimed, so she scanned the room searching for something that could marginally be identified with appointments in her own home. The chintz curtains of the port-hole came closest. She pointed them out to Alice.

'Yours are less flowery,' Alice said. She wondered why Ellen was so desperate to stay in her cabin, since she could see no logic in it. She wondered whether Mr Bowers had anything to do with it. She wished she knew the number of Mr Bowers' cabin. Perhaps its location had something to do with Ellen's present needs. But there was little point in pursuing that line of enquiry. She pulled out her suitcase and opened the drawers. As she laid her dresses on the bed, she realised, for the first time, what she was forfeiting. For it was not only the room that she was surrendering, but a possible rendezvous. He would come to her cabin, find Ellen there, and make some excuse for his intrusion. Could she count on him to deduce that she had exchanged with her friend? Could she count on his lustful appetite to outlast the stretch of corridor, the flight of steps, the twisting gangway to her new quarters? She began to hate Ellen a little. Her friend's selfishness could well ruin all Alice's chances. She threw her clothes into the cas.

'I'll carry your dresses on the hangers,' Ellen said. She wanted to be obliging. 'No sense in getting them creased.'

And so Alice and Ellen swopped cabins with Alice's dresses drooped over Ellen's arm, and Ellen's on Alice's on the return journey.

The waiter was watching them, unseen, from the top of the gangway. He smiled, put his hand in his pocket and fingered his screwdriver. From his long experience of cruise-women of a certain age, he was confident that neither friend would confide in the other. He knew he ran no risk with the one known as Alice. He already sensed her ambivalent appetite for him and he knew, too, that any lust on her part would blunt his own. It was the other one who drew him, the risky one, the rigid, cold, ungiving one, who could be relied upon in her rigidity. It was she whom he wanted. Yet he wouldn't let Alice down completely. He would visit her from time to time. She was still respectable enough at least never to demonstrate her appetite. He watched Ellen lead the way back to the cabin, lugging her suitcase behind her. He would wait until they both went into dinner. And he would remove the chain from Ellen's door. Then both ladies, up and down the deck, would be at his nightly bidding, for his nightly choice, and in his nightly terror, and he laughed aloud.

During the day, Ellen and Alice stayed on deck, moving between the dining-room and the deck-chairs. Ellen, who was utterly exhausted from her night's vigil, slept most of the afternoon in the sun, and when she awoke she felt not in the least refreshed. Yet the thought of an uninterrupted night heartened her. And then, for the first time, it crossed her mind that he would go again to what he thought was her cabin and find Alice there. Oh my God, Ellen thought, what have I done? The thought that he might rape Alice simply because she was any old object in a bed made poor Ellen tremble with treachery. She could not put her friend's life at risk; she would have to tell her the whole story, and they could huddle together, both of them, in one cabin for safety.

She rose from her deckchair and looked round for Alice and recognised the back of her leaning alone over the rail watching the sea. She noted how her friend's skirt drooped on one side and how in the middle it was caught in her buttocks, in such age and such innocence that it would have denied with profound indignation and incredulity any story of a sexual encounter simple and straight as it might be. But rape would claim no credence whatsoever. Alice simply wouldn't believe it, Ellen knew, so there was no point in telling her. She tried to convince herself of her own specialness, that it was she and only she that the caller wanted. He would be satisfied with nothing less. How could she have thought for one moment that he would be interested in Alice? No. Alice was safe. She kept saying it to herself over and over again. At last, she almost believed it. She decided she would return to her cabin and take a bath before dressing for dinner. She crossed over to the rail and stood by Alice's side. Alice did not hear her approach, neither did she seem to sense a presence at her side. Ellen looked at her. She was far away, in a dream of her own, scored by the waves lapping the ship and the cry of the gulls in its wake. Her smile was wistful, and an onlooker might have thought the lady were in love, but Ellen thought that Alice was getting old, old enough to recollect her childhood, and perhaps her first sight of the sea.

'Penny for them?' Ellen said.

Alice started, and reddened, fearing that her friend had read her mind of its filthy thoughts, and heard in her ear their filthy words, and sniffed their smell stronger than the brine of the sea.

'I was thinking of when I was a little girl,' Alice innocently obliged, 'and when we went to the sea for bank holidays.'

And Ellen was sorry that Alice had suddenly grown old. 'Have you seen Mr Bowers?' Alice said, bouncing the dubious ball into Ellen's court, though she knew that on Ellen's side of the net it would be unsullied enough, and she felt rather sorry for her.

'Not since breakfast,' Ellen said, 'but I've been asleep most of the afternoon.'

'I saw him,' Alice said, scoring a point for her cabin eviction. 'He was playing shuttleball with one of the stewardesses,' and she turned her face back to the sea, and sniffed its brilliantine tang once more.

'I'm going to my cabin,' Ellen said coldly. 'I'll see you at dinner.' She walked slowly along the gangway. She was filled with an overwhelming malaise. Her friendship with Alice seemed suddenly threatened, and she felt herself to blame. Mr Bowers was off with a stewardess, prettier perhaps, and certainly younger, and Ellen felt suddenly very alone. But what isolated her most was the knowledge that she could tell no-one, no-one at all of the outrageous assault on her poor person. If only she could confide in Alice and be assured of her credulity. She thought of Walsh and Thomas, and out of respect, in separate breaths, hoping to glean some happiness from their recollection. But they only served to confirm her extravagant widowhood. There was no-one she could tell except herself, which she did, over and over again and each time with greater anger and larger loathing. It was the untellable tale that bruised the spirit, and she closed her cabin door behind her, fondling the chain and finding a little comfort in its promise of protection.

Alice turned away from the rail and made her way to her new quarters. Her brow was puckered. She feared that he might not guess at her change of cabin and that thought deeply disturbed her. He would look for her, she decided. He must find her. She would will it. As she closed the cabin door, she noticed the absence of a chain. And suddenly she was terrified. She had to have a choice. Even if she chose the terror, and all the thrill that that terror entailed, she had to have the right to bar its entry. Once she had resented the presentation of choice; now its absence equally offended her. Like Ellen before her, she looked around the cabin for something portable that would hold the fort against him. But there was nothing. She sat trembling on the bed. It is God's will, she said to herself, and thus fortified by divine sanction, she surrendered herself to his invasion, and though terrified by her vulnerability, she dared to hope at the same time that he would find the right door.

Mr Bowers was waiting for them at dinner. He remarked with concern on Ellen's pallor, and enquired as to her health. Her terrible story gathered on the tip of her tongue, begging for release. But she swallowed, and declared herself very well thank you but a little tired. Mr Bowers took similar note of Alice's high colour, which Alice was quick to attribute to the sea air and a general feeling of well-being. When he suggested his usual post-prandial turn about deck, both ladies declined. Both were anxious to get back to their cabins, the one for yearned-for sleep and oblivion, the other for the tremblings of expectation. They kissed each other good night on the cheek, and Ellen felt considerably heartened by the obvious renewal of their friendship. She looked forward to a long night's rest, and perhaps in the morning her pain would have eased. She closed her cabin door, and automatically felt behind her back for the chain. She groped blindly and with growing panic. She dared not turn to look and to acknowledge the plain fact that it had gone, and not, it was plain, of its own accord. That it had been taken away, and clearly by him, and equally clearly for his own ends. And that spelt out only one purpose. A return visit.

Ellen began to cry. She stared at the door. He could come at any minute. If she couldn't lock her cabin, then all she could do was in some way to lock her body. To this end, she decided not to undress. Moreover, she would dress more fully, arm herself with clothing, so at least it might delay the final assault. She rummaged through her drawers. Underneath her underwear she found a corset, a rarely worn garment that was necessary only for one dinner gown, that was slightly too small for her. She looked upon its pink whalebone as a blessing. It was a suit of mail, almost, and would certainly stave off, or at least delay, a fatal blow. Quickly she screwed herself into the garment, covered it with three skirts and a number of blouses, and her cardigan. On top of it all she put two evening dresses, and covered the whole ensemble with a brown mackintosh. It did not occur to her innocent self that the impediment of clothing, and a whalebone corset to boot, would only serve to stoke the fires of her attacker's ardour, and, as she added layer upon layer, she felt more and more secure, ramparted, bulwarked against any attack. And very hot indeed. But survival was worth sweating for. She was fully prepared. She even lay on the bed and waited for him.

And so did Alice, her eye fixed on the door-knob, terrified of its sudden turning, her hot loins full of hope. He would come at any moment and in her new chiffon négligée she was ready for him. As she'd slipped it over her head, she'd told herself that she was wearing it for herself, for her own pride and vanity and that it was incumbent on any woman of a certain age to keep herself attractive, if only for her own sake, and she lay on her bed, fingering the soft folds of ribbon on the bodice, and hoped that it would be pleasing to his eye. He'll be here soon, she said to herself. He's delayed by all the duties he has to attend to. And she saw him as a worthy citizen, full of his responsibilities, her knight in shining armour, and she, as his willing adversary.

But Ellen was not willing, heavily armed as she was, and when he saw her lying on the bed, weighted by the strata of clothing he would have to penetrate, all the pathetic water-proof, shock-proof, man-proof lines he would have to breach, his body trembled with his lust. As a preliminary, he showed her the photograph once more, smiling, as if to remind her of the conspiracy to which she was party. Then he said, 'I think

92

I'll have a change tonight.' He stuffed the photograph back into his pocket, and leaning over the bed as the smile vanished from his face, he said, 'Turn over.'

Alice waited, allowing for all the duties that had to be done. She saw him coming to her, exhausted by his work and begging for her comfort. She waited, her eye on the door-knob. It was dark outside, and silent. She was tired, but she kept her vigil. She lay, her eyes wide with fear and hope, until she heard the gulls shrieking a new morning. He won't come now, she whispered to herself. He has found someone else; and she turned her face to the wall and wept.

And that was how he found her, in disappointed sleep, without hope of his ever coming again. He looked at her flimsy nightdress and he knew she'd expected him. After the moats of clothing he had recently crossed, the drawbridge of corsets, the ferry of waterproof, Alice presented nothing to him, but her sad see-through availability. He pitied her profoundly. And out of that pity, and for the sake of something to do to round off his night, he lay down beside her and went about his business.

CHAPTER SIX

The other Alice

On the morning of the fifth day of sailing, the weather changed. A positive wall of heat hit the passengers as they left their cabins for breakfast. And affected them all. Suddenly the cruise had become a serious proposition, and its Mediterranean geography amply proved by the weather that the brochure had promised. The cruise frocks were duly aired, and men's sporting clothes, geared to earnest holiday. Good weather can often lift depression, or at least postpone it for the rainy seasons. Alice Dove was thus affected by the climate change. On deck, in the morning haze, Nellie's image was a blur, and Richard's a mere negative of her loss. She welcomed her sense of sudden well-being, and knew she must act on it for she did not trust it to endure. She needed to share it. In the deck-chair at her side, her mother held her face to the sun, her eyes closed in daydream, transported to the distant safety of her childhood. So that when she heard Alice's voice, she was confused, unable to place its sound in the location of her mother's gentle home. Then she heard the words of that sound, and their mildness was even more confusing. She opened her eyes.

'I'll go back to the cabin and get your swimming things if you like,' Alice was saying.

'I think that's a lovely idea,' Mrs Dove stammered, bewildered by her daughter's sudden change of mood. Alice had actually suggested that they do something together, something pleasurable. Moreover, she was going to do a favour for her mother. She was going all the way back to the cabin, and in this heat, too, to fetch her pool-attire. Alice was being more than accommodating. She was being solicitous. Mrs Dove shut her eyes again, unable to believe it, assuming that their recent unsoured exchange was part of her daydream that for some reason had been interrupted. Then she felt a hand on her arm.

'I won't be long,' Alice said.

When Mrs Dove dared to open her eyes once more, Alice was gone, and she was content to ascribe the whole exchange to her own fantasy. But for the print of Alice's hand on her arm, that seared her skin with throbbing undeniable autograph. That could not be attributed to dreaming. Mrs Dove dared to hope that the small gentle words, that had passed between them, signalled a turning-point in their cruising, and that the next three weeks would be at least bearable. Perhaps there would even be moments of pleasure.

Alice Pickering, on the other hand, had not yet noticed the change in the weather, for she still lay a-bed, curled up and thoroughly and delightfully ashamed of herself, savouring the afterglow of her dawn encounter. Ellen too, was still a-bed, but even if the tropical sun had sweated her sheets and shone buttercups under her chin, she would have been sublimely indifferent to its gentle caress. For her depression was paralysing, her unhappiness so undynamic that it was frozen. She tossed and turned with a pain equal to her rage. It had been an horrendous assault. The poor armour of her total wardrobe had served only to increase his ardour. She tried not to think about it, but the pain that throbbed through her whole body, and threatened at times to split it in two, would not allow her to think of anything else. It was a persistent pain with no let-up, and she wondered whether she would ever walk again. She knew she must get up and try, for there was no calling for a doctor, or for Alice, or for any help from any quarter. Once again she thought of going to Alice and weeping her heart out, and caring not for what Alice thought. But she realised that, after the night's performance, Alice's presence in the cabin was no guarantee that he would refrain. Indeed he had almost hinted at it himself. Or had she imagined that? But she distinctly remembered hearing his laughter as he threw out the suggestion, even mentioning Alice by name. She wondered whether he knew her name too, and that thought disturbed her even more than the pain. The act itself that he had perpetrated was horrible enough, but the idea that her name could be identified with it shocked her profoundly. An act, per se, was of no news value unless its participants could be named. But once identified, the act was available to the general ear, to rumour abroad, to public sighs, abomination and disgust. She would endure the pain, Ellen decided, she would learn to live with the damnation of his assault, but she would never survive its publication.

She eased herself out of the bed and hobbled to the bathroom to run a bath. Water she knew as a balm for aching limbs, and slowly she undressed the crumpled skins of her wardrobe, piece by piece. As they piled up on the floor, she managed a pale smile at their total uselessness, and immediately she felt prepared to face a new day and bide her terrible night until revenge was possible. For never for one moment did she cease to think of her private retribution. She climbed carefully into the bath, and sat down gingerly, and then, for a long time, she dwelt on the joys of slowly and painfully sending him to his death. It was already late, and she wondered why Alice had not come to see why she was still a-bed. She thought it uncaring, but she was nevertheless grateful to be released from the obligation of explaining her breakfast absence. She took her time with dressing and putting away her brave armour, and it was almost lunchtime before she was ready. And still Alice had not come. Now she began to wonder whether Alice too was indisposed, and for what reason. She would go and investigate.

Walking was not easy for her. Her thighs ached, and it took her some time to get to Alice's cabin. On arrival, she knocked and entered without waiting for a reply. Alice was still a-bed, though awake now, a smile of reminiscence playing on her face. This she quickly removed on seeing her visitor. It was shameful enough to be caught in bed at such an hour. It was blasphemous to be seen to be enjoying it.

'What's the matter?' Ellen said. 'Are you ill?'

Alice almost wished she could oblige, to give her laziness some reasonable excuse, so she feigned a poor night with fitful sleep.

'I didn't sleep too well either,' Ellen said. 'I've only just got up myself.' She sat on Alice's bed and smiled at her. For no specific reason that she could fathom, she felt a great warmth for Alice at this moment. Her presence gave Ellen some assurance that she would survive the untellable trials that nightly awaited her, that she would avenge herself with honour and with glory, and that the two of them would return to their welded homes and cruise-reminisce, with omission on Ellen's side, over the garden wall. It did not occur to Ellen that Alice would have anything to hide. She took a strange pride in the knowledge that, however terrible his act, he had chosen her, Ellen, née Head, then Walsh and, for a short time, Thomas, to be his partner.

'Are you getting up?' Ellen asked.

'In a minute.' Alice did not want to uncover herself while Ellen was looking, in case there were any leavings of him in the bed. But Ellen made no move. Alice sidled out of the sheets and put on her dressing-gown. 'I'll meet you in the dining room,' she said.

'I'll wait for you if you want,' Ellen said, wondering why Alice had become so suddenly independent.

'You go and find Mr Bowers,' she said. 'He must be looking for us.'

She's sending me on an errand, Ellen thought, and then preferred to think that Alice was sending her away because she was shy. It was easier to accept that explanation rather than acknowledge a reversal of roles. So she took herself on deck to look for Mr Bowers.

Alice wallowed in the bath. She felt no pain in her limbs, and she marvelled at how quickly the body attuned itself to new and unaccustomed experience. Her love had come at dawn, and there was the wonder of romance in his timing. He had heralded her day, and would, with luck, all her days, till the ship docked for the last time. His timing gave her the added bonus of a night's sleep. She could with confidence shut her eyes at night in full expectation of his dawn awakening. Yet with all her content, some small irritation nagged at her. It was Ellen's face, and the pallor and pain of it. There was no question in Alice's mind that her friend was not well. Yet she did not seem ill in the usual sense; her malaise appeared to be very much of the spirit, and Alice wondered what was troubling her. Her first thought was of Mr Bowers and the possibility that he had rejected her. She had seen him the day before with the stewardess, but had thought nothing of it, because all the stewards, male and female, mixed with the passengers for recreation. But Ellen had not seen him the whole day, and their dinner together had been silent and almost sullen. Mr Bowers had claimed a headache and so had Ellen, and Alice had been a little impatient because you were not supposed to feel unwell on the health-giving cruise that the brochure had promised.

She got out of the bath and dressed hurriedly. She had to talk to Ellen. She did not feel entitled to her own happiness if her friend was troubled in any way. She was relieved when she found Ellen and Mr Bowers at their usual table in the dining-room, leaning towards each other as if in intimate conversation. She almost felt an outsider as she took her seat.

'Mr Bowers only just got up too,' Ellen informed Alice.

'We are a trio of lazybones,' Mr Bowers said. 'We must make up for it after lunch. I suggest a turn about the deck and a splash in the pool.' His words dived onto the table and gave an indication that Mr Bowers was no mean swimmer.

'I can't dive,' Alice said, putting herself immediately out of competition.

'Neither can I,' Ellen said, aligning herself with Alice's aquatic inadequacies.

'But you can swim?' Mr Bowers said.

Both women nodded though without appetite. Once in the pool they knew they would enjoy it. But it was the costume that attended such a sport that they found unnerving, and both scratched in their minds for some excuse to withdraw.

'I don't like the chlorine,' Ellen said with sudden inspiration.

'I much prefer the sea,' Alice followed her opening, though Alice had never been in the sea in her life. The Ilfracombe waves terrified her, and she always longed for a chlorinated pool where you could see and know that your body was still attached to your legs.

'Oh do come,' Mr Bowers was saying, as if he owned the pool. 'It will do us all good. We'll walk off our lunch around the deck, and then we shall take the waters. I shall be most disappointed if you do not join me.'

Ellen and Alice felt they could no longer refuse, and each recalled the shape and size of their swim-suits, lying on the bottom of their cases, as a mere cruise formality, and never meant to be taken seriously. Alice's suit was many years old, and had never come into contact with water, chlorinated or otherwise. She had used it occasionally for sunbathing, and even then she had covered it with a towel. Ellen's was black with *Ilfracombe* written diagonally across it, as if, at some time or another, she had been its carnival queen.

Alice looked around the dining-room and imagined the women passengers in bathing attire, and she felt equal to any of them, and fairer than most.

'Alright,' she said. 'We'll join you in the pool.' She had answered for Ellen too, and Ellen was satisfied, because it meant that Alice would take full responsibility for the adventure and even for the stupid *Ilfracombe* that was blazoned across her body.

After lunch, they retured to their cabins for their piscine preparations. Alice put hers on without looking, her eyes tightly shut. She felt the stretching latex over her skin, and its emphasis on all the folds of her flesh. Then blindly she moved towards the mirror and opened one eye. It seemed to her that she looked much better naked, and that the swim-suit was an obscenity, calling to everyone's notice the fold between the thighs, the clefts between the breasts and buttocks which, left to themselves, without any trappings, would have suggested no more than the body's simple structure, with no invitation to experiment or abuse. She quickly covered herself with her dress, and prayed that her dawn-caller would be nowhere near the pool.

In her cabin Ellen was trying to unpick the *Ilfracombe* corsage of lettering. She started on the 'I', but after a few stitches she discovered that the letters were not attached, but were part of the fabric itself. Quickly she re-stitched it, and tried it on. Unlike Alice, who had come to understand her body as an object of loving, who was able to view it with pleasure, even if only with one eye, Ellen felt towards herself an increasing revulsion. The women were reacting in diametrically opposed fashion to exactly the same agent, though neither knew of the other's connection. Ellen forbore to look at herself in the mirror. The most she could manage was a downward glance that ascertained that everything was in its right place. She covered herself with a dress and went to meet up with her companions on deck.

'Just a brisk walk to get our lunch settled,' Mr Bowers said and he took their arms and paraded them proudly about the deck. He reckoned on two turns for their digestion, then offered to race them to the pool. Ellen thought that was very unseemly, and said as much, and Alice was getting rather bored with Mr Bowers' athletic promise.

'Then we shall walk at a brisk trot,' he said, which he did, while Ellen released her arm and took her own slow pace which had hardly quickened since morning.

When she reached the pool, Mr Bowers was already taking an unnervous stand on the diving board. She was surprised at how skinny he was. Not a bit like Walsh or Thomas, she thought, who liked their pint of beer on an evening and were not ashamed to pay in fat for it. Nevertheless the fragility of his body appealed to her, and she began to worry that it might disintegrate on its impact with the water. He stretched out his arms and was seen to take a deep breath. Then, in a second, his long body lay like a fish under the water, with a heart-stopping stillness, and then flicked its wrists into motion. She watched him through the water, and wondered what he was using for breath. At the end of the pool, he turned, and never for a second lifted his head, and he swam like long velvet to the other end. There he slowly raised his head, and took in a soft breath like a woman. He saw Ellen watching him and he smiled. 'Come in,' he shouted.

'I'll get ready,' she called back, panting, and she realised she had been holding her breath on his behalf, and in his interest, for most of his two-length swim.

There was no sign of Alice at the pool, and Ellen surmised that she must still be changing. She went into a cabin and took off her clothes. Then covering her seaside location with a towel, she ventured into the air and reluctant display.

In the pool she noticed Mrs Dove, splashing like a child in the shallow end. Then she saw Alice, gingerly descending the pool steps, and she waved to her. Ellen dropped her towel at the edge of the water, and immediately drew the attention of Mrs Dove who declared Ilfracombe her home town, with the implication that that was a basis for communication and even friendship. Ellen was grateful. She had fully expected her identity tag to be a source of ridicule and she stepped into the water and carefully made her way to the daughter of Ilfracombe for protection. She was surprised at how light-hearted Mrs Dove looked, quite unlike the morose figure who nightly hugged the dining-room wall.

'We used to spend our holidays in Ilfracombe when the children were small,' Ellen said. 'It was lovely.'

'Have you met my daughter?' Mrs Dove said. In view of her Alice's sudden change of mood, she was no longer reluctant to advertise their relationship. But her Alice was nowhere to be seen, and Mrs Dove feared that the magic had run its course.

'I don't see her,' she apologised timidly to Ellen. 'She must have gone back to our cabin. We share one, you know.'

Ellen envied her. Mrs Dove had one hundred per cent security. If she were ever to have a nightly visitor, the taboo of blood would cry out for blood, where friendship might hold its tongue.

'Are you enjoying it?' Mrs Dove pressed on.

'Oh yes,' Alice joined in the conversation, and Ellen echoed her sentiments because there was no point in denying them. She couldn't imagine what Alice found so enjoyable, except perhaps the food which she seemed to relish. But so far she had taken little part in the cruise activities and retired early. Perhaps it was the mere change that she was enjoying. It was a change that poor Ellen could happily have done without. She didn't know how she would survive until their scheduled return. She had thought of leaving the boat as soon as they got to Venice, but she didn't have enough money to make her way home. Besides, she would not know how to explain her sudden departure to Alice. Most important of all, she would not, for one moment, give up her solid intention of revenge, but how or where, she could not fathom. But she had to keep its possibility in the forefront of her mind. It was the only thought that kept her from losing her sanity.

'Shall we swim to the other end of the pool?' she said.

Mrs Dove confessed that she dared not go out of her depth. Besides she was disturbed about her Alice's sudden disappearance and wanted to keep an eye out for her. Alice Pickering would have preferred to continue their conversation, but she rarely said no to Ellen. So she nodded, and together they started off to the end of the pool. They did a stately breaststroke that had not improved in style since they had first learned it in school, in the days when Alice went into chlorine by order of the curriculum. They kept their heads and hair-dos well above the water-line, screwing up their faces with the effort. When they reached the end of the pool, they clung to the rail, panting. And in their line of vision, standing on the edge of the pool, was a pair of patent waiter's feet. And they both knew to whom the feet belonged. They looked up, knowing that they shouldn't. He smiled at them, and with consummate nerve, he said, 'Are you enjoying yourselves?' Both women reddened. Even in the cool of the water they could feel the sudden flush in their bodies. Alice's was the blush of young love, while Ellen's was the fever of fury. Neither answered, but turned and breast-stroked away, each questioning the other's lack of response. They saw Mr Bowers at the end of the pool and both swam towards him for his sundry offers of safety.

Ellen leaned against the rail and dared to scan the perimeter of the pool for her assailant. Alice did the same, both pair of eyes skinned for any gesture on his part that betrayed a familiarity beyond his so-called waiter's calling. He was serving drinks to the passengers around the pool. He seemed to have a smile for everyone, but Ellen noticed that it lacked the conspiratorial wink that she had seen in his disgusting eye, and Alice noted its lack of tenderness that she had seen especially for herself at the end of the pool. On the evidence, both women felt themselves singled out for his attentions, and both reddened on its account.

Mr Bowers' female entourage was breeding. He now found himself happily surrounded by his two faithfuls, joined now by Mrs Dove and her Alice. Mrs Dove's fears regarding her daughter had been well-founded. The effect of the climate-change was short lived. Soon enough the sense of loss and confusion, that Richard and Nellie engendered, once again disturbed her partly-numbed spirit. She had gone back to the cabin to change into her unconvinced dungarees, and she returned to the pool her raging relentless self.

'This is my daughter, Alice,' Mrs Dove meekly apologised.

In ordinary circumstances Alice Pickering might have been slightly disturbed to share her name with another, since it was one of the few aspects of her person in which she had some measure of confidence. She had grown as Alice, habituated herself to its sound, possessed it, and it, her, and to share it, especially in a competitive social arena, could have been threatening. But in the circumstances, it did not trouble her.

There was only one Alice on whom her dawn-visitor called, and he possibly did not know her name any more than she, his. It occurred to her that their shared anonymity was a spur to their lust, and Alice Dove, however she was called, could never be party to such a connection. She looked too prim, too rigid, a little like Ellen, Alice thought, then chided herself for her treachery.

The group withdrew from the pool, and arranged themselves around a parasolled table on the terrace, and they were hardly seated before the waiter approached to take their orders. Mr Bowers spoke for them all. 'We're not yet decided,' he said. 'Could you return?'

The waiter bowed, with eyes for all and none of them, placed a drinks' menu on the table and went away.

'What about a bottle of cold white wine between us?' Mr Bowers suggested.

The ladies seemed satisfied with that choice and grateful that it had been taken out of their hands. All except Alice Dove, who lost no opportunity, however trivial, in asserting her independence. 'I've spent twenty years of my life,' she said, 'being ordered about, ordered for, and I'd like it known that I have my own mind and my own tastes. I'll have a Campari,' she said.

The rest of the company drew their own conclusions. Behind Alice Dove's assertive vocabulary, so they were to learn later, and from the biased party of her mother, lay the ruins of a broken marriage. But in Alice Pickering's eyes, it was Alice Dove who was the marriage-wrecker, and a graceless one at that, and she fully sympathised with the husband who could take no more of her. Ellen's sympathies, on the other hand, were on the woman's side, and she bristled once more with liberation thoughts, now more clearly defined by her nightly assaults. Mr Bowers murmured an apology for his blanket order, and Mrs Dove looked across at her daughter and was ashamed. Not only had she revealed an intimate detail of her life, but she had put an end to the trivia of conversation which was what a cruise was all about. There were endless subjects that could be peripherally debated without betraying one single aspect of one's private thoughts. It had been Mrs Dove's way all her life. Occasionally she wondered what all her pains and stresses were doing, for she did not doubt their presence. She heard them, distinctly, and outside herself, shuffling about their business, treating their unhealable wounds. Sometimes she actually watched them, answering their own door, making their own tea, but not for long, for she feared their infection, as a leper might another's sores. Why couldn't her daughter keep her pains to herself? Millions of women had been left by their husbands, but they hadn't joined movements as her Alice had done. They hadn't marched about cities, screaming their private rage in public slogan. They hadn't found friendships with other women which were beyond the limits of sisterhood. Poor Mrs Dove shuddered at the thought of that Nellie, whom her Alice had temporarily left to do her filial duty by her mother's widowed holiday. She saw Nellie in her boiler-maker's suit, and her closely cropped hair, and wondered why, if Nellie hated men so, she wanted so much to look like them. She was grateful that her Alice still wore the occasional dress, but nowadays she looked lovingly at her daughter's long up-pinned hair as if she was seeing it for the last time. But quickly Mrs Dove put away such thoughts, sending them to join the others, to tend their own wounds.

The waiter returned. 'We'll have a bottle of Chablis,' Mr Bowers said. 'And one Campari.' He tried to give as much dignity to the side-order as to his own choice, but it sounded like a rough uncultured postscript to a love letter.

The waiter looked at Alice Pickering, staring at her. And Alice lowered her eyes, waiting for him to go. She could not return his gaze, at least not publicly, else it would have implicated her. She looked at Ellen and hoped that she knew that what the waiter did with his eyes was his own business, but Ellen had seen his look and she wondered whether he had Alice in mind for his next victim. She could not help hoping that this might be the case, for together they could more easily destroy him.

There was a silence around the table. Alice Dove had made it clear that she would brook no trivia. Mr Bowers, forever dwelling in the deep end, decided to take the plunge. 'Don't you believe in marriage?' he said, staring at the Campari, which the waiter was at that moment placing before her.

Not now, both Ellen and Alice prayed. Not in the waiter's ear-shot. They noticed how he hovered, waiting for the

Campari response, but Alice Dove wished to take full advantage of it, because in her mind he belonged to that same species that had broken her back over the years and she had enough rage to spill on the whole of his gender. 'I think it's an institution of enslavement,' she said.

Ellen nodded her head vigorously but gave no verbal assent, for she was sure of the principle though uncertain when it applied itself to Walsh or Thomas. Alice thought that her namesake was ridiculous. The very word enslavement thrilled her, and it was all she could do not to look up at her lover and exchange what was surely a common opinion. The waiter was uncorking the bottle. He took his time with its pouring, no doubt waiting for Mr Bowers' come-back. And, as if to oblige, Mr Bowers said, 'I myself am a widower, but I look back on a very happy marriage, and I doubt whether my dear wife ever thought of herself as a slave.'

'We have only your word for that,' the Campari said.

The waiter poured a little extra wine into Mr Bowers' glass as some compensation for the insult. When women's swords are drawn, gender will out, irrespective of its proclivities. He replaced the bottle in its ice-bucket, bowed and moved away, but no-one sensed any conversational freedom in his absence for it seemed that there was little left to hide.

'You may be right,' Mr Bowers said graciously, 'but if she had felt enslaved, I think she might have left me many years ago. We had no children, you see, and she was a woman of private means. She had no practical or economic reasons to stay with me. I surmise that she was therefore as fond of me as I of her.'

Through want of an adequate response, Alice Dove sneered, and there was silence again. It seemed that the first round in what was clearly going to be a battle had gone to Mr Bowers, and Ellen, despite her fondness for the man, felt that he had won it more by courtesy than policy.

'There are exceptions in marriage,' she said. 'Like anything else.'

'I'm sure you had a good marriage though, Ellen?' Mr Bowers said.

'Oh yes,' Ellen said quickly. Divorce and enslavement happened to other people and she was not prepared to give it any more thought. Though it was a woman like Alice Dove she needed as a confidante. If she could tell her the whole story, she might well offer to be an accomplice in her revenge. It was clear that Alice Dove had daggers in plenty, but her target was too general for the bull's eye. She might well have welcomed a specific quarry, and Ellen began to wonder how she could broach the subject. But all the time she feared for her own image in another's eye. Even Alice Dove, brainwashed as she was to man-hatred, would not help but deduce, from her story, Ellen's own complicity.

Alice Dove had given up the battle. She recognised it as no fertile ground for conversion. But she noted with a little concern, how quickly her evangelical appetite could wane. Her heart was not in it. Never had been, if she were really truthful with herself. Her own conversion had been a negative one, simply because, after the break-up of her marriage, there seemed no logical alternative. She thought of Nellie who never in her life had been enslaved by any man, or even loved without enslavement, but who was devoting her own colonising energy to bullying other women. Alice amongst them. She was disturbed, too, for another reason. As the waiter had placed her Campari in front of her, he had brushed her hand as it came forward to hold the stem of the glass. Had she timed her move for that accidental touching? She could not deny her attraction for him, as if there remained in the bowels of her sloganised pamphleteered spirit some simple neurotic need for male piggery. She looked around the terrace for some sign of him, but he was gone.

Mrs Dove looked at her daughter and sensed that she had withdrawn from the fray. She was overcome with pity. Her child, and she still saw her as a child, did not even have the courage of her own convictions, for those convictions were clearly unconvincing. She pitied her daughter's limbo, her rootless unalignment, and then she quickly put the pain of her pity aside, where it joined the Dove battalion of wounded.

'Are we all ready for the fancy dress party?' Mr Bowers said, and his change of subject sounded desperate.

'I haven't thought about it yet,' Mrs Dove said, 'It's difficult if you're away from home with no means of finding any disguises.'

'I notice that one shop on board sells masks and things,'

Alice Pickering said. She had her own disguise prepared and so had Ellen, secretly hidden from each other at the bottom of their suitcases.

'Well you have a week to rummage round for something,' Mr Bowers said. 'And the theme is very flexible. People who have changed the course of history.'

'That depends on one's political opinion,' Alice Dove said with a sneer, and her mother looked at her, hoping to God that her daughter would not fancy-dress according to her politics.

'Perhaps you can find something in Venice,' Ellen said. 'Depending of course on your opinions,' she added, with a shrug in Alice Dove's direction knowing that little could be found in that chauvinistic city that would answer to her requirements.

There was silence again, and it was saved, if one could call it rescue, by the sudden appearance of Wally Peters, his ample paunch drooping over his thighs, and almost obscuring his black shorts. He drew up a chair without invitation. He knew the Doves – Wally probably knew everybody on the boat, and had been quickly tired of by all of them. He was now no doubt making his second round. He placed himself next to Alice Dove who made a slight move of her chair, not so much to accommodate him, as to avoid the possibility that his dripping flesh might touch hers.

'May I treat you all to a round?' he said, prepared to buy his way into their circle.

'Not for me,' the ladies declined, unwilling to pay his price, and feeling a slight chill in the air and wishing to get back to their cabins to change.

They rose, the four of them, a united band, and excused themselves, leaving Mr Bowers to deal with Wally and the bill. As Ellen left the terrace, she was satisfied to see that the waiter was still on duty. She thought she might snatch a little sleep before dinner, for she was certain that her night would once more be disturbed. For a moment she stood outside herself and wondered how she was able to endure it. That woman who lay trembling, brutalised each night in her bed, was some other Ellen, and that Ellen made her angry with her total submission. Yet there was nothing she could do about it except feed on thoughts of revenge and so sustain herself until the cruise was over. Once inside her cabin, she lay on the bed, and within minutes she had fallen asleep. Alice and Mr Bowers missed her at dinner, and afterwards Alice felt free to walk the deck with him, since she was in no danger of missing her caller.

After her promenade she made her way to Ellen's cabin to ascertain that all was well. Ellen lay fully clothed on the bed in a deep and lightly-snoring sleep. Alice covered her with a blanket, and still she did not stir. She tip-toed out of the cabin and went to her own. There she bathed, scented and chiffoned herself and fell asleep, confident that, when the gulls screeched the dawn, he would awaken her. She thought of Ellen and hoped that she would sleep through the night and that hunger would not awaken her.

But Ellen did wake, shortly after midnight, and not for want of food, but for the sniff of brilliantine.

CHAPTER SEVEN

Two attempts that failed

The following day they arrived in Venice. The boat docked early. Ellen awoke as the light broke through the port-hole, surprised that she'd been able to sleep at all. Her body was stiff but there was no soreness. She began to fear that she was getting used to her torture, and that in time she would not feel it at all. And that growing numbness might finally blunt her appetite for revenge. So she sat up in bed and fed her rage. She recapped each and every one of his actions since he had first come to her cabin. She concentrated on each minute stage of his procedure, and she was horrified to find that already she regarded them as an outsider. They had become events, each single sordid one of them, mere happenings in the past. They had become a tale almost fit for the telling. She clenched her teeth with what was left of her rage, and in doing so felt a sudden and excruciating pain in her jaw. She tried to open her mouth but its aperture was hardly large enough for the rim of a cup. She swallowed and felt a muscular pain in her throat. She sucked in her cheeks and the pain brought tears to her eyes. She was convinced that she had broken her jaw, and that during the night, for some reason she did not know, she had been called upon to perform an act far beyond the jaw's natural function. She started to cry with the recollection. Now she knew why her body did not ache, why she was on the point of almost forgiving him. But now, remembering what he'd made her do, what new variation he had concocted for his filthy pleasure, she no longer had any need to feed her rage. She would get up, disembark at Venice, and go to a shop and buy some means for his execution.

She rose from her bed and set about her toilette with firm resolution. In the bathroom she rinsed her mouth for a long

111

time, sipping the water through the small hole that she could muster, and she feared that never would she be thoroughly cleansed again. She was still rinsing her mouth when Alice knocked on her door.

'It's me,' Alice said as she came in. 'Are you ready? We're docking soon.'

'I won't be long,' Ellen said through the small hole of her mouth, so that her words were clipped and whispered.

'Are you alright?' Alice called.

'I've got a blister in my mouth,' Ellen said between her rinsing. She was satisfied with her excuse. It would do for Alice who was very gullible, and would believe anything.

'Oh you poor thing,' Alice said. 'Perhaps we can buy something for it in Venice.'

Ellen came out of the bathroom and Alice was disturbed at the way she looked. Ellen, on her part, marvelled at Alice's complexion, the moist peach glow on her cheek and the light in her eye, so unlike the Alice she knew from the hedge-clipping days. She looked at her without envy. All her natural malice had now been channelled into one single and supreme purpose, focussed on one target, and one alone, the life-centre of her assailant.

'Dry land will make a change,' Alice said, hoping that something solid beneath Ellen's feet might infuse some strength into her body. She really was looking quite dreadful.

'I'll wait for you on deck,' Alice said, seeing that Ellen would be slow with her dressing and needed no witness.

The passengers were gathering along the rails for a sight of Venice in the distance. They were to have a whole day in the city. Alice caught sight of Mr Bowers. The Dove partnership hung loosely at his side, and Wally Peters, less secure, had actually taken his arm. It was the sight of the latter that decided Alice to steer clear of the group. Besides, she thought, Ellen, in her frail state, would probably prefer to spend the day in small company. She moved to the far end of the rail, well out of their sight, and stared at the murky waters of Venice docks. Despite the oily streaks on the water, the flotsam of waste and sewerage, the cacophony of hooters and sailors' oaths, she found all of it beautiful. Inside herself she felt a young girl, breathless with curiosity and an utter conviction that only other people were mortal. Part of her joy

112

was her secrecy. She had no appetite to tell anyone of her love; she had no urge to put him on show. She felt conquered rather than the conqueror and she was glad to be his prisoner. She tried not to think of the time when the cruise would end, of her return to the terraced house, of the dawns that would break undisturbed. She knew she had changed beyond any point of return. She could not now go back to her old way of life, to her uneventful days. Only for a while would his words still echo in her ear, and in time they would pollute the air beyond her hearing. She tried not to think of it.

She felt a tap on her shoulder, and she turned, expectant. She hoped that Ellen didn't see the disappointment on her face.

'Have you seen Mr Bowers?' Ellen said.

'He's down the other end with the Dove women. And that Wally. D'you want to join them?'

'I think there's a guided tour,' Ellen said. 'We ought to take it otherwise we won't know what to do or where to go.' Ellen had suddenly become quite helpless. There was no hint of her former fiery independence that had so irritated Alice at times. She wanted to be led, to be taken by the hand.

'Let's do that then,' Alice said, and she took her arm solicitously and guided her over to the Bowers' contingent.

Mr Bowers gave Ellen a great welcome, both for her own sake, and the fact that the presence of the Doves and the insistent Wally was stretching even his limits of courtesy. The younger Dove sneered at him silently and continuously, and Mr Bowers found her mother's shame hard to bear. Every time her daughter opened her mouth, Mrs Dove mouthed a pre-emptive apology. He took Ellen's arm. Perhaps he too noticed her pallor and sensed her need for attention. She clung to his arm as to a life-raft.

Their guide was marshalling them towards the gangway. Other groups, ahead of them, had already boarded the vaporetto that would take them to St Mark's Square. At the top of the gangway Ellen turned, sensing a presence behind her. The waiter stood there smiling, slipping his hand into his inside pocket. With her eyes she begged him not to display her. But he took out the photograph nonetheless, covering it with his coat and stealthily showing it to her. 'I'll see you tonight,' he whispered. She was so grateful for his whisper,

113

that she did not at first realise what he'd said. Then she shivered and clutched Mr Bowers' arm and almost pushed him down the gangway.

She had to do something about her predicament. There was something infinitely stupid in voluntarily entering the torture chamber night after night and awaiting one's punishment. Yet short of telling Alice, which was more and more unthinkable, she knew there was nothing more she could do. She counted on her fingers the remaining nights of the cruise. They totalled sixteen. Sixteen new and terrible variations, sixteen threats to her life. And, even if she were maimed beyond repair, she could call no ship's doctor to attend her, and the thought occurred to her that she would not survive at all, and the only precaution she could take was to spell out in a letter to Alice the whole sordid truth of it. Her bruised broken and totally dead body would give the lie to Alice's suspicions of her friend's complicity. And Alice would see to everything. She would take revenge, legally, decently, and with timid indignation. Yes, she would compose a letter as soon as the Venice tour was over. This thought, even though it was of penning her own obituary, comforted her a little, for it represented something she could *do*, for what was so unbearable in her situation was her total impotence. She dared to look back at the gangway as they reached the dock. He was standing there, watching her, his hand resting on the inside pocket of his jacket. From that distance, he seemed to be looking after her with a certain longing, as if, during the course of the day, he would miss her profoundly.

She turned away quickly. *Dear Alice,* she said to herself, *I did not die a natural death as all the doctors will tell you. Over the last few days, I have been coldly and systematically murdered.* She clung to Mr Bowers' arm and boarded the vaporetto.

When they disembarked at St Mark's Square, their guide stationed himself on a small stone platform on the edge of the canal. He was silent, but his positioning indicated authority, and the cruise passengers gravitated towards him, bunching around his person, the better to hear his sermon. And sermon it was, at least by its tone, which was full of admonition and dire warnings. The story he painted of Venice's present condition sounded very much like the passengers' responsibility. It was their fault that the city was floundering into the

114

sea. They looked at each other, ashamed, and, not able to bear the accusation in the other's eye, looked at the ground which seemed to be sinking beneath their feet. Ellen found the man's tone extremely irritating. She had not come to Venice to be berated. Indeed her mission had nothing to do with history, with Venice's past or its questionable future. She was here for arms' shopping and, until that mission was accomplished, she could devote thought to nothing else.

The group were already moving towards the cathedral, when Ellen disengaged herself from Mr Bowers' arm. 'I feel like staying in the fresh air,' she said, her eyes on the shops that ringed the piazza.

'But you must see the cathedral,' Mr Bowers said. 'It would be infinitely worth your while.'

Ellen thought that Mr Bowers had no notion of what her while was worth in the present circumstances, and she certainly could not risk any dilution of her feelings for revenge by a visit to a house of God and its notion of turning the other cheek.

'I might go in later,' she said. 'We have the whole day here.' Despite their guide's warning, she was confident that the cathedral would not drown during the course of her stay.

'But you'll miss all the information,' Mr Bowers said. He was clearly disappointed in his pupil's aptitude.

'We can look at the shops later,' Alice said, then regretted it, for she realised that for some reason Ellen needed to be on her own. Then quickly she said, 'Where shall we find you?'

'I'll be here on the square,' Ellen said. She pointed to an open-air café. 'I'll meet you there,' she said.

She watched them follow the group into the cathedral, and as soon as their backs were turned, beyond looking once more over their shoulders, she hurried to the far corner of the square and started to case the shop-windows. She moved from one boutique to another. Occasionally she paused and worked out the prices in the currency she could understand. She was horrified at her deductions, and wondered whether her small allowance would stretch to her simple ammunition needs.

Most of the shops were concerned with clothing and, after her first price comparisons, held little interest for her. She did not know exactly what she wanted or what kind of shop would approximate to her needs. So she wandered from boutique to boutique, until she reached a gift store with windows jumbled with goods in great variety. She went inside.

There was a central table devoted to mementos of Venice, but since she had seen nothing in the city, there would be nothing to jog her memory, so she passed by quickly and, in doing so, knocked one of the souvenirs off the table. She turned to pick it up and, when she saw what it was, she knew it as an omen. It lay on the floor and practically spoke to her. She picked it up gently. Whatever it cost, she would pay in full. In gold letters over a crest, it proclaimed itself a souvenir of Venice, though it had absolutely nothing to do with the city, or any other city for that matter. In as much as it was a souvenir at all, it was a reminder of camping, picnics, or sheer downright murder. She cradled it lovingly in her hand.

On the cash counter was a card declaring that, amongst other languages, English was spoken. But Ellen needed no words for what she was about to do. The transaction, from its purchase to its final use, would be a silent one. She took note of its price on the label, and wordlessly handed over a sheaf of lira. The assistant looked at the gift and smiled, assuming she had a grandson, and Ellen ran out of the shop, fully armed and trembling. She made for the open-air café at the end of the square. She did not expect them to join her for some while, which would give her time and peace to examine the means of her assailant's disposal. She reached the café and took a seat at a corner table, her back to a trellised partition which offered a little privacy. She mouthed 'Coffee,' to the waitress who approached her almost before she had seated herself, and settled down to investigate the pamphlet of instructions. The information was in several languages, a fact she found strangely comforting, since it indicated that people all over the world might have the same murderous intent as she. On the second page, she found the English version. There was a long list of functions for which the gift could be put to use. She did not expect to find her own purpose listed, or anything near as lethal. Its twenty or so catalogued uses were to do with merry-making, carousal and over-all preparedness. It was an instrument designed more for survival than

116

execution. But it's *my* survival, she said to herself, and that thought blunted all scruple.

It was, to say the least, de luxe, the Rolls Royce of scout knives, with eight sharp blades, and a corkscrew. She concealed it on her lap, and slowly opened out each single cutter, with a view to choosing the one that would most effectively fulfill her purpose. There were various lengths and widths, and when the knife was fully spread, its murderous fan glinted in the sunlight of the square. She covered it with her hand, and shivered. She realised that there was no question of a choice of blade. She would use them all. Like any good scout, she would be fully prepared. She would skewer him on her Sheffield plate octave, and like a cat, give herself eight chances of survival. She looked at the fan spread out on her lap, and was afraid to touch it. If she clasped it in her hand, it would be by way of rehearsal, and rehearsal could only lead to performance. And despite all her imaginings over the past days, all her mise-en-scène for revenge, she could not see herself as its director. The act had become acutely premeditated. She had thought of nothing else. From minute to minute she had schemed it; she had paid out good money for its means. She had prepared everything for its rehearsal. She saw herself in the dock. 'I did it on the spur of the moment, m'lord. I just happened to have an opened eight-pronged knife on my bedside table.' She touched it gingerly, and withdrew the last of its functions, a small corkscrew. Immediately the knife took on a benign air. It spelt carousal and merry-making as the pamphlet had promised, and had nothing to do with what she had in mind. Very carefully she folded all the blades and left the corkscrew exposed. Then she put it in her bag. It's a present for my grandson, she consoled herself, and tried not to think of its extravagence.

The waitress put the coffee in front of her, and a small chit beneath the saucer. She would not look at it. She was worried at the rate she was so liberally spending, and all to no purpose. She turned her mind again to means of revenge, a method that would entail his death without her participation. Again she thought of reporting the whole story to the ship's authority. But she had already left it too late, and such delay would not support the truth of her tale. Besides, there was the damning evidence of the photograph. And then suddenly it all appeared to her to be so simple. All she had to do, was to get hold of the photograph and destroy it, without his knowledge and therefore without risk of his terrible retribution. She shuddered at that possibility. She tried to outline a strategy. On past evidence, even as recent as that morning, he always carried the photograph in his inside pocket. She tried to recall whether or not he took his jacket off for each performance. She had never noticed that detail, so she had to devise a pick-pocket plan whether on or off the model, and both presented what seemed insurmountable difficulties. She knew she would have to play it by ear, and with this new plan in mind, she comforted herself. A small bout of petty thieving was infinitely preferable to murder. She was so convinced of her success in this manoeuvre that she began to rehearse the speech she would deliver to an astonished and outraged purser. She would excuse the delay in her report with an offer of her shyness, and her repeated hope that it would not happen again. But it had now become a nightly performance and it was slowly killing her. She hoped the purser would not ask for details, and that, slowly and quietly, without trial or publicity, he would pack her assailant under his arm, and at nightfall, would throw him into the sea. She would stand at the rail at the purser's side, and watch her assailant flailing his useless arms in a plea for mercy. She would look at the small oil-slick that seeped from his brilliantined head, and she would throw him a comb with infinite satisfaction. Then she would turn from the rail, and go back to her cabin and sleep without fear.

She was smiling when Alice came towards her.

'It was lovely,' Alice said. 'You should have come, Ellen.'

'I needed the fresh air,' Ellen said. 'I'm feeling much better now.'

Alice sat down beside her.

'Where are the others?' Ellen said.

Alice nodded in the direction of the cathedral, and Ellen spotted Mr Bowers with Mrs Dove on his arm, and the angry Alice bringing up the rear with Wally Peters at her reluctant side. They converged on Ellen's table. Wally drew up more chairs to accommodate them. 'My round,' he was saying. 'What will you have?' He looked at Alice Dove, 'Apart from your Campari, of course,' he added.

Ellen thought that Wally Peters was asking for trouble, and Alice Dove thought likewise, but couldn't be bothered to oblige. She was thinking of Nellie, not with love or nostalgia, but with anger at the thought that Nellie's brainwashing had landed her in such emotional confusion. Wally Peters' gender did, after all, represent half the human species. And they were not all like Wally, or that Bowers man, or to go to extremes, her own husband, who had left her for one of her own gender. Women weren't necessarily superior, as Nellie kept bleating in her daily harangues. Nor were they necessarily beautiful, another of Nellie's slogans. Anyway, there was no law that men should be cleverer than women, so it was no crime if they weren't. Yet women, out of their own sad conditioning, mocked man's ineptitude, and labelled him inadequate. She no longer knew the quality or sign-posting of her appetites, or indeed whether she had any at all.

'You missed a treat,' Mr Bowers said to Ellen.

'I've had a lovely time,' Ellen defended herself. 'Sometimes one needs to be by oneself for a while.' This last with a pointed look in Mrs Dove's direction and her arm which, for reasons other than support, was still entwined in Mr Bowers'. She stared at it, and Mrs Dove, sensing her own trespass, hastily separated herself.

The waitress came back to the table and took their orders.

'We have an hour at least before we gather again. There's still time to go to the cathedral, Ellen,' Mr Bowers said. 'I'll take you myself when I've finished my coffee.'

'That would be very kind of you,' Ellen said, and felt suddenly that, in the light of her new-found solution to her dilemma, she was able to renew her appetite for Mr Bowers' solicitousness. 'I'm ready when you are,' she said.

'You will excuse me ladies,' Mr Bowers said. 'I'll leave you in Wally's capable hands.'

Nobody questioned that, neither did they confirm it, but, however capable or otherwise his hands, they shared a common hope that he would keep them to himself.

Alice was very confused. She couldn't understand Ellen's sudden change of mood. Perhaps it was because she did not like to be part of a crowd that she would not join the fold that followed their appointed shepherd, but wished to be singled out for guidance. Alice thought that Ellen was being very superior, but she would not think badly of her. Her own sense of well-being was too acute to allow for malice. The after-taste of her lover's dawn visits lasted through her whole days and nights, and merged with the excited anticipation of his coming once more. She hoped that Ellen was enjoying herself in the cathedral and that Mr Bowers was holding her carefully on his arm.

She finished her coffee, or rather started it, for both beginning and end were achieved in one polite gulp, and Alice thought that foreigners had very strange eating habits.

Wally Peters was silent, shifting uneasily in his seat. His coffee too had been consumed in a single gulp and he wondered now what to do with his hands that Mr Bowers had deemed so capable. Ever since the night of the ship's dance, he had avoided Alice's eye, and she, who had found comfort elsewhere, felt vaguely sorry for him. She caught his glance, though he had by no means thrown it, and she smiled at him. Quickly he smiled back, taking it as an invitation to renew their contact, and the smile faded on Alice's face, fearful of his gross over-reaction.

'Here they are,' Mrs Dove suddenly cried out. She had kept her eye on the cathedral door ever since Mr Bowers and Ellen had entered it. She had no doubt timed their sojourn there and had shut out of her mind all imaginings of how they were spending their time. In their absence her gaze had been fixed in their direction. She was afraid to look elsewhere for fear she would catch her daughter's eye and that look of vacant desolation. Her Alice had said not a word since they'd left the ship. She had been faintly grateful for that, knowing that whatever Alice said would usually shame her. But her daughter's silence was more painful, for it signified a lack of any appetite at all, even for her towering rage; it suggested her hopeless withdrawal from the battle she waged with herself. Mrs Dove could not resist a need to look at her daughter, and when she did, a lump clotted in her throat. And unlike all her wounds till now, this one refused to go away. With all her desperate swallowing, it refused to be put aside. Mrs Dove had no notion of how to deal with it. She put her hand to her throat and saw how her fingers trembled. She felt her daughter looking at her, turning her vacant stare in her direction. Then Mrs Dove lowered her hand and watched it quiver towards her daughter's arm, where it came to rest on her wrist, and through the lump in her throat, she said, 'Are you alright, Alice?'

Alice looked at her mother's hand with the surprise of one who was seeing it for the first time. And indeed she had, in that position, for the hand that Alice knew had never strayed for touching. Now not only did it touch, but it clung. Almost imperceptibly, but there was no doubt of its insistent adherence. Although her mother's gesture was prompted by her concern, it seemed to Alice quite the reverse, as if that liver-pocked hand was pleading for attention, for care, for solicitude. Alice withdrew her wrist from the contact. 'I'm fine,' she said, because she knew that that was all her mother could accommodate. And the lump in Mrs Dove's throat went away, and joined the explosive commune of griefs that dwelt apart. One day, Alice knew, her mother would blow, and she knew, too, that she herself would be the cause.

Mr Bowers and Ellen returned to the table. Ellen looked radiant. 'I'm so glad I saw it,' she said to the company in general. 'Mr Bowers is a wonderful guide. I've never heard so much history.' She giggled with pleasure, and Alice Pickering was pleased she was part of their group once more.

Their official guide, who was moving from table to table on the piazza, now joined their party and offered to escort them to a gift shop, where they could buy souvenirs of Venice. Mr Bowers declined. He was not a souvenir man, he declared. 'I remember all I wish to remember,' he said. Ellen agreed. She wanted no mementos either, but not for Mr Bowers' reason. She suspected the guide would take them to the shop she had already visited, and she didn't want to be recognised and her lethal purchase be recalled and publicised. They would take a walk along the main canal, Mr Bowers said. Alice, on the other hand, was a great souvenir hunter. Her mantelpiece was cluttered with memories of Ilfracombe, and a day-trip that she and Pickering had once made to Boulogne. She took Mrs Dove's arm, and urged her towards the shops. Wally tagged behind. Mrs Dove looked at her daughter. 'I won't come,' Alice Dove said. 'I'll stay here a little longer.'

They moved away, and Ellen and Mr Bowers too, and Alice Dove was left alone at the table.

She stiffened her body. Inside herself, she felt her body

weeping, her nerve-ends glistening with her tears. But they would not flow. Even when Richard had left her, before her bitterness, before her hate, when her stubborn love for him still held sway, even then she had been unable to cry. Then Nellie had come to her, poor Nellie whose monstrous childhood had exhausted all her tears. Nellie wouldn't allow Alice to cry. No man was worthy of one single tear, so Nellie said, stemming her own wall of grief in the strait-jacket of her boiler-suit. She had given Alice love to heal her wounds. Each night as they lay together, Alice told herself that this was what she wanted, that there never was, and never would be any other way. With Richard she had been living a lie. He had done her a favour in leaving her. He had forced her into self-confrontation. And Nellie had confirmed it. But in the day-time, when she was alone, and Nellie at work, it was Richard she missed, and she longed for Nellie to return and obliterate her self-deceit, and willingly dispel her doubts. Over their months together, she craved for Richard less and less, but this did not ease her. Now she mourned the loss of love-appetite, that thirst that Nellie could not slake. She feared that never would she love again. She had talked herself into man-hatred, as Nellie had taught her, though she found no logic in it. She knew that Nellie was a trap, and it had seduced her because she knew of no alternative. She could not face being alone. Her mother's cruise invitation had seemed at the time to be some kind of solution, and she had accepted it gratefully. She knew that she and her mother were strangers, and certainly at this time she would not have wanted it otherwise. She didn't want confidences, she didn't want intimacies. Above all she did not want touching. But what she did want, she was hardly conscious of, and it startled her each night when she went to bed, to hear herself involuntarily mouth to her pillow, 'Please God, for God's sake God, let me love a man again.'

She looked around the square. A young man leant against a pillar and was eyeing her. She looked at his handsome face with an indifference that was sublime. She looked at her hands curled in her lap, and noticed a small liver-mark on her knuckle. She felt a single tear in her eye. It welled there, too proud to fall. 'But I'm only 38,' she said to her hand. She rose, mortified, and made her way towards the water.

The young man left his pillar and followed her, keeping his distance, casting his long shadow in Alice's steps. She watched its silhouette as it moved to her rhythm, and she saw that her own shadow dogged nobody. No-one even crossed it. A small boy ran in front of her. Did she imagine it, or did the child actually stop short and run around it, giving it a wide berth as if it were the plague? Her shadow was like herself. Untouchable.

She made for the vaporetto stop on the edge of the canal, not knowing why, for she had no intention of taking a ride. But she needed to idle by the water, to look down into its murky depths and see not even a blurred image of herself. The absence of reflection was a comfort. It confirmed her own sense of limbo.

At the water's edge, her shadow lay behind her and the young man stood inside it and watched her loitering. He didn't think she was waiting for the boat. Hers was a loitering without intent. He kept his eye on her, or rather on her bulging handbag, and all the tourist goodies that it promised. He was nervous. He cast a sidelong glance at his partner, an older man, who waited amongst the other waiting passengers, legitimising his concern. The young man hovered for his signal. His partner would wait until the moment was opportune – long and successful experience had given him a superb sense of timing – then he would raise his hand to his head as if to scratch it, and the young man would pounce on his prey, and, in the instant, disappear. This was always the worst time, waiting for the signal, chaining one's impatient frightened feet to the ground. From his view-point he could see both of them. Meticulous positioning had been a major part of his training, and he congratulated himself on his present stance which enabled him with the utmost ease to hold them both in his watchful eye.

The vaporetto approached, and though Alice had no intention of boarding, she joined the line of passengers on the jetty. The young man saw his partner smile. The cover of other people was always a benefit in their trade, and he leaned his body forward, ready to spring. His partner waited patiently, while the vaporetto stopped, disembarked its passengers, and started to take the new ones on board. Alice waited patiently too, but with no purpose. The phrase, 'to take one's life,' passed through her mind, and it struck her as odd, since how could one take one's life if one didn't already possess it? Her life, liver-pocked to boot, was not hers. For the past few months it had not been in anyone's keeping. It belonged to nobody, least of all to herself, and was thus not for the taking. This thought for some reason cheered her. It would legitimise what she suddenly had in mind to do. It would even lend it virtue. She would destroy no private property; she would merely be defacing public domain.

She waited until all the passengers had boarded, and she stood still on the jetty, isolated, cocooned in an almost tangible pain. She waited for the vaporetto to take off, as the partners gazed at her, knowing that they'd lost their chance, and fearful of her visible untouchability. She stood there watching the vaporetto out of sight, then she loosened her shoulder-bag and placed it on the jetty. The partners looked at it, lying there, for anyone's pickings, if anyone dared. Then they looked at each other and shrugged. It was all too easy. It entailed no risk, and it was risk that minimised the sin. It was risk they could take to their confessional and offer up as a mitigating circumstance. They stared at the bag lying there, appalled at the waste, and then at its owner, as she, with infinite calm, walked towards the end of the jetty, taking just one more step beyond its wooden limit. As she touched the water, she surprised herself with her last conscious thought, a wish, now too tardy, for the talent of loving. It was not Nellie's face that etched her inner eyelid as she sank; it was Richard's whose betrayal struck her with a lightning flash, which then blacked out completely. The partners watched her disappear and crossed themselves, not so much in respect for her passing, but that they had refrained from plundering one who was already so grossly pillaged.

A crowd gathered at the jetty, screaming for help. Their cries drew the shoppers from the piazza who swarmed onto the quay-side. Amongst them was Mrs Dove. She saw her daughter's handbag lying on the wooden slats, her plastic bequest, and the tears welled to the rim of her eyes, and obediently went back where they came from.

The young man, bereft of his catch, looked down at his new white linen suit which he had bought with the profits of his last snatch, and saw in its voluntarily soiling a passport into

124

heaven, and an exemption from confession for the rest of his life. He dashed to the end of the jetty, and dived in.

Alice had risen twice during the quay-side commotion, her face blackened by the accumulated mud-years of the city's main thoroughfare. When Mrs Dove saw her daughter's face, she gave a small cry, and as the young man reached her and clasped her by the shoulders, Mrs Dove collapsed, unable to witness further. She did not see her daughter dragged to shore. She did not see the young man lay her daughter down and straddle her body with his own. Wally Peters was suddenly conscious of his capable hands, and he lifted Mrs Dove to her feet, and practically carried her to a nearby bench. There he laid her down and fanned her, and looked around for some support. He caught sight of Mr Bowers and Ellen on the edge of the crowd, but they were too glued to the sight of Alice Dove's possible resurrection to pay heed to any diversion. He called their names, but could barely hear his own voice above the din and he cursed them because he'd been landed with Mrs Dove's lack of countenance, and was missing out on all the fun.

On the quay-side, the young man was diligently at work and the crowd watched him with admiration and cries of encouragement. The handbag still lay by Alice's side, and the young man's partner x-rayed it with rage. The travellers' cheques, the countless credit cards that tourists were wont to carry, now lay forever outside his reach, and when a woman stepped forward to retrieve it, he turned his head away.

'She's one of our party,' Alice Pickering explained to the crowd, though few of them understood her. 'I'll look after it for her.'

'Poor girl,' Ellen whispered to Mr Bowers. 'What a silly thing to do.'

The young man was pumping Alice's chest, and as he did so, he squeezed her nose, and laid his beautiful mouth on hers, breathing his life into her in an ecstacy of confession. The crowd suddenly gasped. Alice Dove was seen to open one eye, and then shut it just as suddenly, as if what she saw astounded her. The young man's mouth cleaved to her own, and she felt a stirring in her limbs. And, without being able to help herself, she responded to his kiss and held his young lips on hers for a long while. Then he raised his head, bewildered, attributing her response to her gratitude for deliverance. She opened her eyes and smiled at him. He did not know that he had delivered her from much more than the murky waters of Venice's main drag.

The ship's courier had by now made a belated appearance. He shoved his way past Ellen and Mr Bowers, and both smelt the drink on his breath. He strode over to where Alice lay and stood her roughly on her feet. 'Can you walk?' he said.

She nodded, avoiding everyone's gaze.

'You should get a medal, lad,' he said, turning to the young man who had no notion of what he was saying. So he patted him on the back to indicate his congratulations. He thought that the young man should receive some kind of reward from the party concerned, and would have laid it out himself had he had any notion of what Alice Dove's life was worth. Because, in his mind, reward had to reflect worth. When he was not couriering for Mediterranean cruises, he was a part-time insurance agent and he knew about such things. 'Come with me,' he indicated. He had it in mind to put him together with the Doves, who would deal with the tip between them. Meanwhile Mrs Dove had recovered from her faint and, on being apprised of her daughter's survival, promptly fainted once more. Wally Peters was fanning Mrs Dove and himself silly, and he wished someone would come to relieve him. He hadn't finished his souvenir shopping, and he was irritated that the Doves had interrupted his expedition. He was happy to see the courier making his precarious way towards him, a limp Alice Dove on his arm.

'We'll need a double room at an hotel,' the courier shouted, seeing Mrs Dove's prone body on the bench. Mr Bowers offered to cross the piazza and make an advanced booking.

'Just for an hour,' the courier shouted after him, fearing that he would have to foot the bill himself.

Alice thought that her poor namesake would need a lot more than an hour just to uncake the mud from her hair and body, to say nothing of poor Mrs Dove who would in any case require a little more than time. But Mrs Dove, who had by now recovered, had overheard the time allotted her and she was grateful. It was mercifully too short to allow for conversation, and for her daughter's explanation which she did not want to hear. For whatever Alice would say, shout or

126

weep or plead, she would hear blame in every syllable, acrimonious accusation, that, like an army, hell-bent on revenge, would overrun that separate dwelling-place of her pain, and raze it screaming to the ground. No. She would not bear it.

They straggled into the hotel lobby. Other guests tried not to look at them. A porter showed them to a lift, and the courier shoved their young rescuer after them. 'We'll see you in an hour,' he shouted after them. 'I have to get back to the ship.'

Mr Bowers gave Alice his free arm, for all felt the need for comfort from each other. Even when Wally Peters took Alice's arm on the other side, she offered no objection.

'I think we all need a strong drink,' Mr Bowers said, and he guided them to a table. 'I have it in mind to get absolutely drunk,' he said. Ellen noticed a tear in the corner of his eye, and she put her hand on his.

Mrs Dove and Alice and the young man rose silently in the lift. On the seventh floor they got out and followed the porter to their room. The porter kept his distance. The hotel rarely had guests in such a state and he wanted to remove himself from them. He opened the door and let them in, and did not even wait for his customary tip.

The young man followed the women inside. Alice signalled to him that he could use the bathroom, but he signalled that he would go straight home and use his own. He watched Alice as she opened her bag. And so did Mrs Dove. 'I'll do it,' she said quickly, grabbing her purse, then regretted it, for her daughter's deliverance was her daughter's business. 'I could never pay you enough,' she said, and for her daughter's ear since the young man could not understand.

'I'll see to it, Mother,' Alice said quietly, and her mother watched with curiosity as Alice emptied the contents of her bag onto the counterpane. She sat on the bed, careless of the mess on her clothing, and with a pen, she slowly and systematically countersigned £200 worth of travellers' cheques. They were all she had. Then she emptied her purse of its loose change, unlocked the gold bracelet watch on her arm, and handed it all over to her rescuer.

He shook his head. He wanted no stain on his heavenly

127

visa, but she pressed it on him without a word, stuffing his pockets with a determination that brooked no argument. He took her hand, and kissed it, and did the same with her mother, and then to their relief, and his own, he quickly withdrew.

Mrs Dove stared at her daughter. She now no longer feared conversation. The generosity of Alice's gift had spoken all the words and spaces between the words that neither of them could utter or hint to the other. With her gift, her daughter had declared her joy in being alive, and in that joy she had declared a stake in the future, a declaration, that, for its own fulfillment, had to by-pass blame and accusation. Mrs Dove put her hand on her daughter's arm, then slithered it slowly around her neck and then, aghast at her own boldness, she kissed her on the cheek. Then, fearful of what Alice would do, she fled to the bathroom, and there, sitting on the bath's edge, she decided that her present pain was something she would not put away. She would keep it by her, she would guard it, she would nourish it, and when its strength was unbearable, she would prise open her heart and let it inside.

Outside at the café, Mr Bowers and his party were keeping their eyes on the entrance to the hotel. After a while, they saw the young man bound out of the foyer, and streak across the piazza whooping his delight. Virtue may well be its own reward, Wally Peters thought, but it too, even virtue, has its perks, and he hoped that Mrs Dove would not entirely overlook the part he'd played in her rehabilitation. And he didn't mean with money. Just a little extra attention would do.

When their allotted time was up, and not a moment before, the two women emerged from the hotel. Alice Dove's trousers were corrugated from waist to toe, as the result of an over-hasty, over-heated dry-out. They had shrunk a little and bared the white socks that hugged her ankles. The small white gap at her feet was strangely feminine and betrayed a youth and a vulnerability that Alice Dove had taken so much care to conceal. Ellen and Alice stared at her, and thought that, despite her shabby and stained attire, she looked rather beautiful.

'Let's not speak about it,' Mr Bowers urged quickly, and Ellen and Alice nodded their assent, out of both decorum and

128

embarrassment. The Doves returned to the table and Mr Bowers suggested a last drink before they went back to the ship.

The courier was already stationed at the jetty, with a handful of loyal and dry passengers by his side.

'Champagne, I think,' Mr Bowers said. 'We have life to celebrate.'

Alice Dove was seen to blush and Ellen thought it became her. Mrs Dove took her seat by Wally and took his hand. No words accompanied her gesture, but it was enough to express her gratitude.

'The champagne is my treat,' she said to the company, and she gave the order to the hovering waiter.

There was silence around the table, and all prayed for the waiter's return. Then suddenly Alice Dove said, 'I'm terribly sorry,' and she blushed again, and Ellen thought that her muddy baptism had done her the world of good.

When the champagne arrived and was poured, it was Mrs Dove who gave the toast. 'To the joy of being alive,' she said, and they mouthed it after her. Ellen added her own rider, a toast to her successful manoeuvre that night.

It was late when they got back to the ship and most of the passengers went straight to their cabins. Mr Bowers did not suggest his nightly turn about the deck. His day of chaperoning had tired him. Ellen, too, was glad to retire. She was almost eager now for her nightly visitor, convinced that this night would mark his last call. She did not allow the possibility of failure to enter her mind. The consequences of the attempt, if it failed, were dire and unthinkable. On the tug on the way back to the ship, she had planned her strategy.

She entered the cabin. Her bed was already turned down, and she was alarmed to see his comb lying on her pillow. She was not sure of its import. Had he called and simply left his disappointed visiting card? Or was he, this night, letting her off lightly with just the sniff of him? She undressed and lay on the bed and, almost without any fear, she willed him to come. But when, sometime later, she saw the door-knob slowly turn, her terror returned and for the first time she seriously envisaged the possible failure of her mission, and it crossed her mind to forego the attempt entirely. But she thought too of the sixteen nights of torture that she faced as an alternative. She gritted her teeth.

He entered, smiling, and crossed over towards the bed. Ellen stretched out her arms to pull him towards her. The gesture threw him. He had never counted on this one's appetite. Indeed he had relied on her resistance to feed his own. He hesitated, but she pulled him down on her with a strength that surprised both of them. So he did what he had come to do, though with greater effort this time and he had to hiss a lexicon of filth into her ear with loud and monotonous repetition to stoke his failing fires. She felt his slow movements on top of her and she knew she had time. She raised her hand silently, and placed two trembling fingers into his jacket inside pocket. Within seconds the treasure was in her hands. For a terrible moment she realised she hadn't planned where to put it. Her hand was shaking. To put it under the pillow would cause too much suspicious movement, so she dropped her hand to the side of the bed and aimed it underneath. Her hand was numb with terror. Only the two thieving fingers throbbed with life at all, and these she lay beside her and knew that the deed was done, and that, within a short while, she would arrive, screaming and triumphant in the purser's office. She felt very detached from the proceedings, and she watched him pumping away, panting and hissing with monumental effort, and she felt vaguely sorry for him. Finally he was done. He did not rise immediately as was his custom. He lay on her, heavy and exhausted. She shifted with the uncomfortable weight of him, and as she did so, she recalled with horror his usual mode of leave-taking. He was wont to rise from the bed, smile, and slip his hand into his inside pocket. And he would show her the photograph once more as a reminder to her of how hopelessly her lips were sealed. She trembled at the thought of how he might punish her.

'I'm expecting a visitor,' she squeaked, with sudden inspiration.

He sprang up, and, without even zipping or smiling, he left the room.

As soon as he was gone, she rushed to the door and listened to his receding running steps. She was panting with her envisaged freedom. She crawled under the bed and retrieved

130

the photograph. Then, to calm herself, she sat down unable to believe her good fortune. In a little while she would go into the corridor outside her cabin, and start to scream. Then she would make her way to the purser's office. She could not look at the photograph so she held it face down against her thigh. Her legs were moist and she took care not to dry them. She dishevelled her hair and hoped that the joy in her heart did not show on her face. Then without looking at it, she tore the picture into many pieces, over and over again until it was shredded. She gathered the pieces together and threw them out of the small slit on the port-hole window. Then she set out on her journey of revenge.

As she opened the door, she saw his outstretched patent leather shoe blocking her way. Her heart stopped. He had discovered his loss and he had returned to kill her. She opened her mouth to scream, but her terror was paralysed and mute. He stared at her more with pity than rage. Then slipping his hand into his inside pocket, like a conjuror, he brought out the photograph she had stolen. Or at least a copy of it. 'And there are plenty more where that came from,' he said. 'I have to take my own precautions, you see.' Then he smiled. 'I thought I'd come back and save you a journey.' He turned and strode away, almost skipping with his triumph.

Ellen closed her cabin door. She was grateful that she was still alive, and that gratitude for the moment blunted the edge of her profound disappointment. She began to cry. She sat on her bed and opened her handbag. Inside was the fictitious present for her grandson. She took it out and opened each one of its blades. She looked at it intently. She knew she would have to achieve some familiarity with it, so that it would no longer frighten her. She must even learn to love it a little, to find in its murderous shape some form of friendship. Then perhaps she could wield it with innocence. She left its fan spread open, and put it in the drawer of her bedside table. Then all her rehearsed screams gathered in her throat, and she opened her mouth wide and gave them their silent and enraged freedom.

CHAPTER EIGHT

A death at sea

The fancy-dress ball got off to a timid start. The band was playing, the buffet supper laid, but there was some shortage of revellers. In fact only one brave passenger had put in an appearance, and he now deeply regretted his punctuality. Stuart Petty was a timid man, happy to pass in a crowd, and standing there alone, exposed, he began to have doubts as to the choice of his disguise. In a throng of people it might have passed unnoticed. His costume had involved little preparation, and even less imagination. He was dressed as Adolf Hitler. Petty was a short man, which, in his chosen disguise, was to his advantage. Normally he was deeply conscious of his lack of height and he had been happy to turn it to some profit. But as he stood there alone, with the band playing, and the stewards hugging the walls, and all of them pretending not to look at him, he felt himself in the dock, accused, apprehended for his choice of costume which intimated his political preferences and perhaps a whole sordid way of life to go with them. He moved to the edge of the ballroom and hugged the wall himself. He decided to hang around until the band had finished its medley, and if no other guests had arrived by that time, to return to his cabin and change into normal attire. He wondered why everybody was so late in arriving.

Most of the passengers in fact were fully dressed in their disguises but they were hanging back in their cabins with last-minute fears that their characters would be duplicated or unrecognisable. Then there came a moment when each thought that enough time had been given to crowd the dance-floor, and at that given moment most of the passengers left their cabins and converged on the ballroom. Mr Petty was delighted when he heard the bustle and laughter at the door,

133

and he turned to greet them as if he were their host. And when he saw them, his smile fairly cracked his face, for amongst the crowd he spotted at least a round dozen of Hitlers and combed-down forelock hints of many more behind. He knew then that his choice of costume was absolutely right and proper. Indeed there was no other way a man could attire himself. He felt the bully rising inside him, and he charged into the fray. When they were all assembled, the ballroom looked like the Hall of Mirrors in Berchtesgarten. With the women, the theatrical costumiers had had a field day. Mesdames de Pompadour and Marie Antionettes abounded. One woman who, for better or worse, already had the face, had chosen to go as Golda Meir, and her simple black dress was draped with an Israeli flag, should any spectator be in doubt as to her identity. Her escort had tactfully shunned the Hitler role and, because he, too, for better or worse, had the face for it, was attired as Winston Churchill and, lacking confidence as well of his identification, he was smoking a large cigar.

It was not until the party was in full swing that Mr Bowers arrived with his entourage. They were late because they had been waiting for Alice Dove, who had had trouble with her chains. She had come as Sylvia Pankhurst. It was Nellie who had suggested the costume. But the name of Sylvia Pankhurst was not for ever on the lips of the post-Venice Alice Dove and, though she was a woman whom every woman could not help but admire, Alice wished she had made a different choice. Alone in the bathroom, she had confessed to the mirror that, though he had by no means changed the course of history, she wanted to go as Rhett Butler in *Gone with the Wind.*

Mrs Dove wore a long plain black dress, and she might have been anybody but for the clumsy clue that she carried in her hand. It was a small test-tube, labelled *Madame Curie.* Wally Peters wore a false moustache, and a Russian fur hat, and hoped with such small ruses to pass as Stalin. Ellen and Alice, whose costumes were unknown to each other until they had met before the ball, had chosen identical disguises, which pleased them both. They were two Queen Elizabeths. The second, for the first, though more history-changing, would have been far too elaborate and costly. The royal name was ribboned across their chests, and they held themselves proudly like two pea-hens, their patriotism swollen by foreign seas. But most impressive of all was Mr Bowers. Because he had the perfect body for it, he was scantily attired in a loin-cloth. With a pair of steel-rimmed spectacles on the tip of his nose and thonged sandals on his feet, there could be no doubt on anyone's mind that he was the Mahatma, and a faint cheer of recognition rose in the hall as he entered. He salaamed in response, and the cheer grew louder, for he was more than dressed for the part. He was actually playing it.

The group moved towards the buffet, to the jangle of Alice Dove's chains. If anyone asks me to dance, she thought to herself, I'll take them off; and then she thought she might take them off in any case, in case their presence precluded invitation, so, like a snake shedding its skin, she shuffled them off and laid them on a gilt chair against the wall. Now she was liberated as Sylvia Pankhurst would have wished, at least in the general sense if not in the particular. For Alice Dove was harbouring thoughts that had little to do with women's liberation. Ellen and Alice, because of their cumbersome attire, but more for their regal status, were delegated to sit at the table and reserve it for their party, while the rest piled the plates high. When they were all settled, they made a motley crew. Stalin was showing an unaccountable interest in Madame Curie, Sylvia Pankhurst was in deep and anachronistic conversation with her namesake Elizabethan, though it was hard to fathom what on earth they had in common, while the other royal was feasting herself with Gandhi who wasn't eating anything at all. Everybody was joining in the spirit of the party, which had got off to such an unpromising start. Mr Petty, the original Hitler, was by now thoroughly at home, and having arrived first, was totally convinced he had invented the character himself. Even Ellen had temporarily forgotten her fears.

The dancing had already begun. The ladies' costumes dictated a demure style of movement and the music obliged with its slow tempo. Mr Bowers' party did not seem anxious to take to the floor. Wally Peters, ensconced with Mrs Dove, was quite satisfied with the turn of affairs and did not wish to risk his ascendancy with any movement from his present position. The two Alices were locked in what appeared to be

135

an intimate conversation. Or rather a monologue on the part of Alice Dove, with Alice senior as an avid listener. After the terror of her close encounter with death, after her resurrection and the added miracle that had attended it, the younger Alice felt in need of some confidante. Not of a counsellor; nor in any office of advice, but just a willing ear into which to pour all the excited confusion of her thoughts. She spoke about her husband and how he had deserted her. Alice was sympathetic. She had only to think of Pickering, and his possible desertion, to feel the pain of rejection. She thought too, because she couldn't help herself, of her morning visitor, and her pain if she discovered that he was crowing another's dawn. She put out her hand and clasped her namesake's. Thus encouraged, Alice Dove told her about Nellie. Slowly, starting with the solace, the understanding, and with some kind of emotional logic validating their final coming together. Alice was in no way unsettled by her namesake's story. She remembered how once, many years ago, in their foursome holidays in Ilfracombe, they had met another couple who shared their table. The Brownjohns. Alice suddenly recalled their name. She couldn't give Mr Brownjohn a face or a forename. But she remembered his wife. Priscilla. They had faced each other across the tables with exchanged looks of bewilderment, glances which Alice, in her later years, could construe as longing. From time to time their hands had touched with prepared and premeditated accident. Their encounter had been one of the most thrilling experiences of Alice's life. So she understood full well about Nellie, and she was curious to know about her further. She prepared herself for a recital of wooing, courtship and loving, but Nellie was clearly not to be equated with any of these graces. According to Alice Dove, Nellie had neither wooed, courted nor even loved. She had colonised, and Alice had been her willing slave. She did not talk about Nellie with malice or with anger. As she recounted their life together, she realised that she could blame Nellie for nothing, that Nellie had fulfilled what was, at that time, a very positive need. She was grateful to her. But she would never go back. She startled herself as she made this declaration. She had given voice to a decision that in her heart she had been loath to make. 'I think you're right,' Alice Pickering said, and, to herself: Poor Nellie.

'What does it matter?' she added, 'as long as you're loving. It really doesn't matter who.' But gender was far from her mind. The 'who', to whom she personally referred, symbolised the difference between rough and gentle trade, between the free flow of filth in her ear and an inhibited silence. It was all loving of a kind, Alice Pickering thought, and it crossed her mind to divulge to her namesake, both for her own pleasure, and by way of a confidence exchange, the story of her dawn romance, but she quickly dismissed it, for it was private and sublimely shameful.

Not so Ellen, on the other side of the table, who, at that very moment, was having similar thoughts: that she could spill into the gentle Mr Bowers' ear the story of her blackmailing terror. For Mr Bowers was on the brink of undeniable intimacy. He was telling Ellen the truth about his marriage. It is possible his costume promoted this honesty, that, garbed as he was in the role of pure integrity, it was time to give the lie to his previous stories of his happily married state.

'I'll tell you something in strictest confidence,' he said.

'Oh I won't tell anyone,' Ellen said, excited, seeing herself regaling Alice with his story later on that evening or, if not so soon, then at least over their garden wall.

'My marriage was not happy,' he said. 'At least, not towards the end.'

'Oh I am sorry,' Ellen said, and genuinely, for Mr Bowers, apart from the pain endemic to his garb, was indeed suffering.

'It's not sympathy I want,' he said. 'I need to tell it to myself. It just helps that you're here.'

Ellen was on the point of taking his hand, but the austerity of his costume forbade such intimacy. She couldn't help wishing he'd come as somebody else.

'She had somebody else, you see,' Mr Bowers was saying almost to himself. 'In the last year or so. We'd been happy till then. Very happy. That made it all so much harder. He was a younger man, much younger than my wife, even, and I felt I could not do battle with him. I did not even want to see him. I thought, if I did, I would kill him. Or at least try. I was eaten with a terrible jealousy. Jealousy makes one cunning. It brought out in me a talent for deviousness that I was totally unaware of until that time. I decided to feign a generosity, though there was mean murder in my heart. She wanted to leave me, for ever, she said. I suggested to her that her decision need not be hasty, and I offered her and her lover the gift of a cruise, so that they could spend time together, a time that would help them come to some conclusion. I decided on a cruise after some deliberation. What attracted me was its confinement; that it was a situation that was conducive to irritation, and in such an environment, people could get on each other's nerves with more speed and accuracy than they might in wide open spaces. My wife was most impressed by my generosity, and I was glad that she did not see the cunning behind it. Her love had made her blind, I suppose, because normally she was a highly intelligent woman. I bought the tickets, and one night after dinner, I gave them to her. She was very excited, and insisted on driving to her lover straightway to give them to him. I was deeply hurt. We had spent a friendly evening together and it was cruel of her so to rudely interrupt it. She left me that night in a state of exhilaration. I began to dislike her a little. I stood at the dining-room window, and watched her get into her car. Her obvious joy was so painful to me that I would willingly have killed her too, for the unhappiness she had brought me. That was my very last feeling about her, for I never saw her again.'

He paused. This time Ellen did stretch out her hand, and laid it on his, trying to ignore the holy loin-cloth on which it was resting. 'I'm sorry,' she said.

'I suppose she was so excited,' Mr Bowers went on, 'that she was driving too fast. She did not even reach her lover's house. He never knew of the devious gift she was bringing him. She crashed into a lorry on her way to him. If it had to happen, I can't help thinking, I wish, for her sake, that it could have happened on her way back. They took her to hospital. There was a chance, they said, of saving her. If she had the will to live, they kept saying. So I told her lover. I ordered her lover to visit her, and it was at her dying bedside that we met for the first time. All my anger was shed. I looked across the bed at his pained anxious face, and I knew I had no other course but to love him. When it was all over, I wanted to see him, again and again. It was a way of keeping her by my side. But the thought quite clearly repelled him. After the funeral I never saw him again. I think by some rough instinct of his, he thought I'd killed her with my generous cunning.' He paused. 'I wondered what to do with the cruise tickets. Had her lover been friendly, we might have come on this journey together as some kind of memorial to her. But I don't think the idea would have appealed to him. He was not willing to share her memory with anybody. So I decided I would come alone, as one *should* go on a cruise. I suppose, alone, so that the confinement irks you less. I pray each night for her, though I'm not a religious man, but I suppose I'm really praying for myself and for the strength to live without her.'

He lowered his head, and Ellen took away her hand as a sign of recognition that his narration was over. She was deeply flattered that he'd chosen her for his confidante, and she hunted in her mind for words of gratitude. 'Yesterday in Venice,' she said, though it now seemed years ago, 'you gave a toast to life. You should have listened to what you were saying,' she said.

He smiled at her. 'You're a very wise and kind woman,' he said. 'But are you wise enough to deal with your own troubles? I know you are disturbed by something,' he said.

It was at that point that Ellen decided to spill her own sorry story. She trusted Mr Bowers to believe her; she trusted him to hear it without suspicion. She would tell it as it happened, the simple truth of it, and run what risk she might of his incredulity. This she did, from the very beginning. She omitted the sordid details of their contact, more for the gentle Mr Bowers' sake than her own, but she managed to give him a general idea of the sordidness of the affair. As her narration continued, Mr Bowers began to sweat. 'It's impossible,' he kept saying. 'It's monstrous. How could he?'

Ellen allowed his small explosions, then continued with her tale. At last, she told him about her vain efforts to steal the photograph, of his punishment that she dreaded that very night, and Mr Bowers was so enraged, he had begun to tremble.

'We must do something about it,' he said between his teeth. 'This very moment. The rogue must not be allowed to get away with it. You must go to the purser, my dear,' he said, taking her hand. 'And I shall go with you. And you shall tell him exactly what you've told me. And I shall be there for your support.'

Ellen collapsed in gratitude and relief. 'You're so kind,' she said. 'My life on this boat has been so miserable.'

'I'll not tolerate it a moment longer,' Mr Bowers said. 'We shall go to the purser this very minute.'

Ellen was wondering how she could excuse herself, when there was a drum-roll from the platform, and the master of ceremonies took the microphone. It was time for the fancy dress parade, he announced, and the awarding of prizes. He asked all the passengers to get into a line.

'We can't miss the parade,' Ellen said. 'Your costume is bound to win a prize. It wouldn't be fair. Besides, if we were to leave now, everybody would want to know why, and I don't want anyone else to know except you. After the parade we can slip out quietly.'

Mr Bowers bought her logic, though he would willingly have forgone the chances of a prize, for his rage on Ellen's behalf was monumental. 'As soon as it's over,' he said, gripping her arm.

Ellen looked at his face. It was blazing with the zeal of his mission, and did much to enhance the authenticity of his saintly role.

He guided her into the parade. The stewards were busy separating the men from the women. The panel of judges had taken their seats on the platform and were already making notes. Alice and her namesake joined Ellen who was standing alone. Alice Dove took her chained place between them, so that each Elizabeth stood an equal chance. Ellen felt a tap on her shoulder. She turned round to find Mr Bowers standing directly behind her in the man's line. 'As soon as it's over,' he whispered. 'We must lose no time.'

Ellen smiled at him. She was suffused with relief that her troubles were at last shared. And happiness, too, on account of the profound intimacy their recent exchanges of confidences had engendered. She knew instinctively that their relationship had achieved some kind of specialness. For a moment she dared to hope that there now existed between them the possibility of permanence. Then she shivered with the thought that the good Mr Bowers might well be deterred by the knowledge that she was not only third hand, but very soiled goods indeed. She began to fear Mrs Dove again. But Mrs Dove had no story like hers to share. She and Mr Bowers had given each other their deepest secret, and their exchange bound them together indissolubly. She looked forward to a night of calm in troubled sleep, and a future in which Mr Bowers was no longer a shadowy figure from the past. She could hardly contain her joy.

Wally Peters and Mrs Dove remained seated at the table, he still loath to risk movement. But a steward approached and playfully dragged them to their feet and ushered them into line. Ellen noticed their temporary parting, and the look in both their eyes. She was glad for them. Now I'll have to get Alice fixed up, she said to herself, her Alice, she meant, her hedge-Alice, whom she thought she knew so well, and certainly not that other one, whose confusion she would never in a lifetime understand She took Alice Dove's hand out of pity.

'Now we want the ladies first,' the master of ceremonies shouted from the platform. 'Would you be so kind as to parade around the floor?'

The music struck up a stately march, and the women obliged, the Mesdames de Pompadour, the Elizabeths, one and two, the single Golda Meir and a handful of Curies. An Amelia Earhardt suddenly came to light, complete with model aeroplane and flying boots. As did a trio of ladies in Victorian dress carrying leather-bound books who repeated over and over again that they were none other than the Brontë sisters. They were too proud to wear a label, and were happy to attribute non-recognition of their parts to sheer illiteracy. The women moved around the floor with a gait that matched their parts, mincing, proud or manly, Alice's chains clanking all the while to the rhythm of the marching song. Out of the corner of her eye, Ellen could see the judges scribbling their controversial notes. If she were a judge, she thought, she would award the prize to her friend Alice, as compensation for the lack of a partner.

The women did a double turn of the floor, and then the judges seemed satisfied. The music stopped and the master of ceremonies introduced the chairman of the panel of judges. That gentleman stood to attention, and promised his listeners that he would make his speech short and come to the point straight away. But his promise was as short-lived as his speech was long. He felt obliged to discourse on the judgement of almost every costume, insisting, time and time again, that judging had not been an easy task. Then he could not resist the usual platitudes about the ethics of winning and losing, by which time he had lost most of his audience who had wandered over to the buffet table for more food. The M.C. nodded to the drummer to bring the wayward back to the flock, and in a rare pause in the judge's speech, the drummer obliged and the black sheep returned to the fold.

The judge took the hint and prepared to divulge the panel's findings. The prize, he said, had been awarded to the costume that had shown the greatest originality, which remark, in the minds of most of the women, could have been personally applicable. The judge was giving nothing away. But there came a further clue. 'By originality,' he said, 'we mean something that is the contribution of the wearer herself, rather than what she has acquired at the costumiers.'

On hearing this, all the Marie Antoinettes, Mesdames de Pompadours and the two Elizabeths felt ashamed, and would have been happy to withdraw from the competition in deserved humiliation.

'With this criteria,' the judge bumbled on, 'we have decided that the chains have won the day.'

It was clear that nobody knew what he was talking about, so he was obliged to clarify. 'The prize for the best ladies' costume goes to Sylvia Pankhurst,' he said.

Alice Dove was stunned. She had never in her life won a prize for anything, not even a booby one. She did not know what look to use to accommodate it. All she felt was ashamed, embarrassed and undeserving. There must be a look for that, she thought, then she realised that that was the look she was most at home with, the look she had worn most of her life, her face's natural reaction to the many blows and the lesser bonuses she had experienced. It struck her as odd that both eventualities merited equally the same look. Yet she couldn't help giggling, a bonus to herself, for something that was so unexpected, so unlooked-for. She was no longer available to disappointment. After her Venice rinse, the smallest detail would stir her curiosity, the most trivial pleasure, her joy. She regarded her prize as one for survival. Her costume and chains were mere incidentals. More pleased even than herself was her mother and she rushed to her side with her untouching congratulations. Both the Elizabeths were happy for her, in the light of what the poor woman had undergone, and, like her mother, both looked upon the prize as divine compensation. Wally Peters added his congratulations, and Mr Bowers, too, though he was late in arriving. Ellen noticed with some alarm that his gait appeared rather slow. His voice, too, was faint and she could only suppose that his role had consumed his heart and his soul.

When the men were called upon to make their parade, he was seen to shuffle into line. Yet he managed to look back at Ellen, and in a frail voice, his eyes ablaze, he said again, 'As soon as this is over.' She smiled at him, and wished him luck, and was stabbed with the fearful thought that her wishes were extended to rather more than his costume.

As the men sorted themselves out for the parade, the sundry Hitlers tried to separate themselves in a pathetic bid for individuality. But there were so many of them, they seemed like standard fare. Stuart Petty, still convinced that he had invented the role, now squeezed it for all it had and goose-stepped the parade, his arm in an outstretched salute. The other Hitlers had the taste to think that tasteless. It was, after all, only a role, and a losing one at that. The goose-step matched the marching rhythm, which did equally well for Stalin. When Churchill tried to match it, however, it was sadly out of time and season. Gandhi ignored it altogether, pacing his still quiet circle like a holy beetle.

It took the judges only one round of the parade to come to a unanimous decision. This time another judge was called upon to announce the result, and he was a man of few words. He came to the point straight away. 'Ladies and gentlemen,' he said, 'the outright winner of this round is the most original. The prize goes, with our greatest respect, to Mahatma Gandhi.'

Nobody was surprised, except perhaps Mr Bowers himself. Or rather, he was irritated, for the prize-giving ceremony would only delay his urgent mission on Ellen's behalf. Besides, he was suddenly feeling rather poorly, with a stabbing pain in his chest. He badly wanted to lie down.

His friends gathered round him with their felicitations. As a group, they felt especially privileged, and there were some in the ballroom who, having noted their inseparableness during the course of the cruise, thought that the prizes were possibly rigged.

The band started to play again as a steward placed two large gift-wrapped parcels on the judges' table and motioned the winners to come forward. Alice Dove waited for Mr Bowers to join her, but he seemed suddenly immoveable. He uttered a long and very polite sigh, then his knees buckled beneath him, his face twisted in pain, and he sank to the floor.

Ellen rushed towards him. 'I'm sorry,' he said, in general apology rather than in the particular, for his eyes were closed. 'No, no,' Ellen whispered. 'You mustn't be ill. Now now. We've got work to do.' And Mrs Dove, who'd seen that sort of thing before, and Ellen and Alice, who, God knows, had had their lessons with Walsh, Thomas and Pickering, turned their faces away. And so did many of the passengers, but for other reasons, and mainly of annoyance. What with the disgraceful shenanigans in Venice, and now this, that particular group was giving the cruise a bad name, and they all felt contaminated by it. They hovered on the fringe of the hall, apart, in the survivors' position, their faces masks of manufactured concern.

A steward ran out of the ballroom to fetch the ship's doctor, who had apparently made an early night. Ellen and Alice knelt by Mr Bowers' side, and rubbed his hands. Then into their shadow loomed the white surplice, ruby ring, and dangling cross of Pope John.

'But he's not a Catholic,' Ellen hissed, boiling with Protestant mistrust. It did not occur to her that the Pope was no Pope either, but he had the costume and he could have fooled anybody, even perhaps those on high. 'What's it matter?' Wally Peters said, turning away. 'It's too late anyway.' The doctor, panting in his pyjamas, gave one look at the prone Mr Bowers, and could only confirm Wally's diagnosis. He suggested a massive heart-attack, which, even under intensive care, would have stood no chance at all. He was sure the coroner would confirm it. Alice and Ellen turned away to weep, and, when they looked again, Mr Bowers was gone, as if spirited away, and the bare parquet boards lay between them like hallowed ground. They looked at each other, their eyes unbelieving. It had all happened so quickly.

144

He and Ellen were all but on their way to her deliverance, and, perhaps, Ellen had hoped, even more than that. Alice took her hand. 'We've lost a friend,' she said.

Ellen thought of the secrets they had so recently shared. His had been by way of a dying confession. She hoped it would ease the passage of his soul. Hers, he had taken with her. The exchange, for both of them, was final.

They got up from their knees and saw how the ballroom had suddenly emptied. The two prize packages lay on the judges' table. One of them was discreetly removed. The band had packed it in, and the stewards were quietly clearing the buffet table. One of the judges picked up the remaining package, and silently passed it over to Alice Dove. Then he too retired, quickly, as if whatever had happened that evening had had absolutely nothing to do with him. Now only their little party was left behind. Wally Peters, who felt Mr Bowers' chaperoning mantle descend on him, ill-fitting as he sadly felt it to be, put his arms about the women and ushered them out of the hall.

On their way to their cabins, they met the purser. Oh I had such a tale to tell you, Ellen thought, and, now, once again, without support, it had become untellable.

'I'm very sorry,' the purser said. 'Mr Bowers was a fine gentleman.'

'It was all so sudden,' Wally Peters said.

And that was what was most distressing, the swiftness of his total non-existence. Soon all traces of Mr Bowers would have been removed. The following morning, his place would not be set at table, his cabin would be closed, his return ticket refunded, and it would be as if he had never happened at all. The group stood in stunned silence. Even Mrs Dove allowed a tear to fall.

'Come to my cabin,' Wally suddenly said. 'We must stay together for a while.' He took Alice Dove's prize parcel and carried it ahead, leading them in slow procession. Ellen noted the chain on Wally's door. Her fears that earlier that evening had waned in the hope of some kind of resolution, now multiplied. She looked around the cabin. There was no-one to whom she could repeat her story. Even if she steeled herself and told it to Alice, there was nothing Alice could do about it. Alice did not have Mr Bowers' authority. Alice was a woman, and together in the purser's office, they would have been mocked and pitied. Her sorrow at Mr Bowers' passing was compounded by her own self-pity. She heartily wished she were back home, safe with her Walsh and Thomas memories.

The sad little group seated themselves around Wally's cabin. They were silent. There seemed nothing to talk about. Mr Bowers' death was much too recent to allow for reminiscence, to permit talk of his virtue, or stories of his friendship. Such tales would touch Mr Bowers with history, and it was beyond their belief that he was not still one of their party. 'What was your prize?' Wally said, for want of something to say, for he was not a man at ease with silence.

'You can open it if you like,' Alice Dove said.

Wally was glad of something to do, and the others glad of something to watch as he fiddled with the ribbon about the box. He was going to take his time, for once the parcel was opened, viewed and commented on, the silence would descend again, and he would be the first to notice it. The women watched him fascinated. In time, he drew off the ribbon and started on the gift wrapping-paper. He was careful not to tear it, easing the sellotape with his thumb-nail. The paper covered a cardboard box, and taking it off, he folded it neatly and put it aside. The dramatic pace of his unwrapping had by now turned it into a performance, a spectacle, an entertainment even, and conscious of its unseemly overtones, he began to hurry, and when he came down to the box itself, he opened it with little care or ceremony.

Inside, on a bed of straw, lay three bottles of champagne. He touched them with the back of his hand. They were cold, as if just removed from the ice. It would have seemed almost discourteous to the thoughtful ship's management not to drink them right away. The same thought passed through the women's minds as at least an activity that would break the silence between them. But none of them spoke of it, for it seemed tasteless to be revelling in the still amorphous wake of Mr Bowers' passing. But Alice Dove, whose gift it was, felt that it was her right to dispense it at her will, and was quick to afford a rationale. 'We'll drink to our friend,' she said. 'He would have wanted that.'

Wally emptied the carton, aware of the problem of glasses.

146

But the ship's authorities had thought of that too. Embedded in the straw at the bottom of the box were three glasses emblazoned with the ship's name in gold lettering. Those, and his tooth mug, would cater for the ladies, Wally thought, and he himself would make do with the bottle. The women were happy to leave it all to Wally. Despite Alice Dove's rationale, they were still slightly uneasy with the proposed celebration and they wished that Wally would get on with it, and quickly, so that the wine would dilute their scruple.

He popped the cork, and a shower of champagne rinsed his hand. Ellen was glad of the waste. It somehow blunted the blasphemy. Wally poured drinks all round, then raised the bottle in his hand. The subject of their toast was made much of, his name repeated over and over again, like a mantra. They drank quickly, holding out their glasses for more, so that his name could be forgotten, at most a blur in their consciousness, and the wine could be drunk simply for its own sake.

Before long the first bottle had been emptied and Wally opened a second. The women were glad he had not asked their permission, for it was he who was leading them on. His was the entire responsibility, but by the time the second bottle was consumed, all scruple was evaporated. Wally began to sing, and for some reason, a Scottish melody, though it had nothing to do with his heritage. It was a well-known ballad, and the women took it up, soulfully and off-key. It was a sad story, of the death of a loved one, which Wally had thought appropriate in the circumstances. It was not until the third verse, after long and painful suffering, that the young sweetheart had breathed his last, and at this point in the song Ellen had begun to giggle and, with that signal, all their pent-up feelings were licensed for release, and they all broke into laughter, raising their glasses in unsteady hands, and tottering to their even more unsteady feet to celebrate in dance the passing of that dreary lover who had taken so many long verses to die. After poor Mr Bowers' demise that had in no way taken its time, it seemed a presumption to make a production of death, to give oneself time to fear or to woo its approach, time to ask for pardon, to confess, to atone, as this wretched Romeo had done over interminable stanzas. Mr Bowers had died as he had lived, decently, directly, giving no

147

trouble, handing out no false hopes. They linked arms, hanging onto their glasses, and described a small unsteady circle around the cabin. After one turn, they sat down exhausted, their glasses drained.

There was one bottle left, and there seemed no point in keeping it. It would have been mean to Mr Bowers' memory if they had been miserly with its pledge. Wally opened the bottle, solemnly trying to control his laughter. Mrs Dove started on another song, in an attempt to bring the party back to some form of solemnity. But her song told an even sadder story than Wally's, an account of a young sailor drowning at sea, a tale so desolate and so melancholy, that it was hilarious, and their laughter was now very close to hysteria. By the time the third bottle had been drained, none of the celebrants had any idea of why they were where they were and to what purpose. Ellen lolled in her chair, her laughter half dissolved in tears, and she whispered the name that those tears dictated. 'Poor Mr Bowers,' she said, and throughout the cabin the name rang a faint and distant bell. It was a sobering sound, and the general laughter which had never been far away from weeping, now dissolved completely.

'We should all go to our beds,' Wally said.

The ladies rose slowly, unsteady on their feet. Somehow or another, they found their way back to their separate cabins.

It was late. Ellen sat on her bed and the full impact of Mr Bowers' loss overcame her. She was not immediately concerned with her intruder. She was convinced that this night, surely, he would not come. Slowly she got into bed, too exhausted and miserable to wonder how she should now proceed. Later on, the door-knob turned in her cabin, and through her half-sleep, she sniffed his brilliantine overture. She was astonished. 'Have you no respect?' she whispered, an unlikely question to one who had little enough respect for the living to spare any for one who was no more. He smiled. 'It won't take long,' he said. It was as much concession as he would give.

CHAPTER NINE

A nameless proposal

The ship was gloomy the next day, and full of whispering. Mr Bowers' little group went about their business of having a holiday. They all wondered what had been done with Mr Bowers and Wally had suggested that, since the poor man had no relatives to whom to give account, they might well have unceremoniously thrown his body into the sea. No-one would ever know, he kept saying gloomily. Which was what upset Ellen most, that there was no family to mourn for him, no child he would leave fatherless, no sibling who would miss a brother. Dying was less than final, she thought, if there were someone still around to mention the dead one's name. She would remember him, she decided. She would talk about him to Alice over their garden wall.

The other passengers on the ship seemed to be avoiding them, for their little group had given ample evidence of being disaster-prone. And so they stuck together, bound by their common mourning. None were unhappy with the situation. They were reasonably at ease with one another. Like a small family, they played cards together, went in a party to the pool and managed to have their meals at one table. Over the course of the next few days, they experienced a growing content in each other's company, and the other passengers thawed a little and from time to time, they joined them. Ellen's heart lightened, and one morning she arrived at breakfast so jubilant that the others remarked on her look of good health and happiness. She had gone to bed the previous night, her eye on the door-handle and fear stalking her body. She must have fallen asleep, and when she awoke it was morning and she realised that he had not come. That her night had been free, and perhaps, she dared to hope, the nightmare was all over. As she dressed, singing to herself, she forgave him, forgave him utterly. As long as he never came to her again, she would pardon him. She had opened the drawer of her bedside-table, and wondered what on earth she could have thought of doing with that murderous fan, and carefully she'd closed it, and put it back into its case. She could not stop herself singing and she tripped into the dining-room like a young girl. Her pleasure was acute, and it was only marred by the sight of her friend Alice who seemed to be in a deep depression.

'Did you not sleep?' she asked.

Alice nodded her head. She had slept, and profoundly. That was the trouble. She had overslept, for no cockerel had crowed her dawn. She feared that it was all over, that he had found another. She kept looking around the dining-room, as if she had lost something, and only when she noticed that Ellen was looking too, did she hastily return her eyes to her breakfast plate. And looking down, she sniffed the brilliantine, and so did Ellen, and both shivered. Before them, a hand poured their coffee, and both of them looked at it as if seeing it for the first time, which perhaps they were since that appendage played no part in their respective dealings. Neither of them looked at him.

'Bit short-handed this morning,' his hand said. 'One of the stewards is sick. Been up all night,' he added gratuitously, no doubt as some explanation to the two women for his absence from their beds.

Wally said he must be tired.

'Yes,' he said. He was about to retire shortly himself, but that evening, he promised them, he would be up and about as usual. This last to Alice and Ellen as his finger pointed in their direction.

'Should dock in Limassol this evening,' he added, 'and tomorrow night we turn for home.'

They knew all that. They knew it from the brochure, and they wondered, Wally and the Doves, why he was making a point of it. They concluded that the man was simply making conversation. But Alice and Ellen heard it as his proposed schedule. Ten more visits to each of them.

The cruise is half over, Alice thought sadly, and Ellen trembled with the knowledge that it had only half begun. They waited for the hand to move away, then they looked at each other and wondered at the sadness in each other's faces.

'I'll be glad to get home,' Ellen said, and the others agreed, as if in tribute to Mr Bowers whose passing had deprived the company of its cheer. But of them all, only Ellen really wanted to be at home with the surety of going to bed each night without fear. Alice dared not think of her return, and the eternity of mornings without her glad awakening. As for Wally Peters, he regretted the small time left to him. Ten days was hardly enough to gain Mrs Dove's confidence, and perhaps a promise of something even more lasting. He had to accomplish that on the high seas, while the romance of cruising could blunt the edge of his ungainliness. For he knew himself to be unattractive, uncouth and unpleasing to a woman's eye, facts which on terra firma were plainly in evidence. The moonlit seas, the nightly music, the total caress of their cossetted ship-board life could happily translate those deficits into traits that were moving and even admirable. In the light of the moon, his unattractiveness could be subtitled as gauche and vulnerable, his vulgarity as frailty. His stage was the ship, but once off it, he would have to join the milling throng of competitors, unmasked, unfrocked, unorchestrated, shuffling along into his lonely night.

Mrs Dove too, was not anxious for the cruise to end. But not on her own behalf. She felt that her Alice needed more time to be with herself, away from Nellie and the confusion that that companionship engendered. Over the last few days she had watched her daughter's face undergo an extraordinary change. The furrows that led from nostril to chin were no longer visible. Except as occasional smile lines. Her eyes sparkled without tears and the anger that red-wealed her neck like an enraged cockerel had faded. Her Alice had become almost beautiful. It was no longer a face for that Nellie who would re-scar it in her own unsure gender. Mrs Dove wished that her Alice would find a beau, and she wished for it on this ship, so that Nellie, and all she stood for, could be rejected before landing. Only then could Mrs Dove look to herself and perhaps to Wally Peters and, in doing so, shut her eyes to his faults, her ears to his vulgarities, and all her senses to his embarrassing availability.

As for Alice Dove herself, the prospect of return excited her. She had not wavered in her decision to leave Nellie. She

151

worried a little about the method of parting, and had decided to return straightway to her own flat and to lie low for a while. Nellie would make contact soon enough. Of that she was sure. She would probably visit. She would not risk the telephone, fearing refusal. But Alice was prepared for that. In fact she would prefer a visit. A parting by letter or telephone was cowardly and by no means as final as encounter. It would not be easy. Nellie, she knew, had been rejected before. She tried not to pity her, for pity would have weakened her resolve. She looked forward to going home, to being alone even, to marvel at the order and the peace that had, with calm insistence, found lodging in her heart. She knew it had happened in Venice. She could only guess at the why and the how, and she did not want to dwell on it. But she knew in concrete terms what it had done for her. She was able now to think of her husband's rejection without the usual accompanying thought of her own diminishment. She was still hurt, but without anger. She knew now that it was a pain that time would heal and that at last, she could now give time, time for its healing. She was convinced that she would totally recover.

'I do miss him,' Ellen suddenly said. 'He was so looking forward to Cyprus. He'd been there before, you know.'

'Poor Mr Bowers,' Mrs Dove said, then after a pause, 'Did he have any family? Brothers, sisters?'

'He was alone,' Ellen said.

'He missed his wife a lot, I think,' Wally said. 'Must have been a happy marriage.'

'Oh yes,' Ellen agreed, rather too readily. 'It was blissfully happy.' Whatever secrets she was party to, Mr Bowers had the right to that kind of memorial. A happily married man who died of loneliness that they called a heart-attack.

'I wonder...' Wally started to speak but then thought better of it.

'What did you wonder?' Mrs Dove said.

Wally looked at the floor. 'I wonder what they've done with the body,' he said.

Everybody wondered and had possibly been wondering since poor Mr Bowers' demise. But no-one offered any suggestions for none of them wanted to acknowledge the finality of his disposal, whatever its means.

'I think I'll go to the pool,' Alice Dove said.

'I'll join you,' Ellen rose from her seat, and Alice, her Alice, stood up, gulping down her coffee. Wally looked at Mrs Dove terrified that she might follow them.

'I'm going to have another cup of coffee,' she said.

Wally watched them out of sight. He smiled. He was having breakfast alone with Mrs Dove. It was like being married.

At least so he thought, for Wally had never experienced the married state. He'd had his chances, as he was quick to offer when questioned as to his bachelorhood. Oh yes, he'd had his chances, quite a few, he'd say, and their fictitious number grew each year in recollection. When he'd reached his forties, he'd resigned himself to his lonely state, and had spent the next ten years fashioning a rationale for his bachelorhood. When he was 55, he'd had a bad car accident, and had been obliged to spend a number of weeks in a hospital bed. His leg was broken and his upper arm. He had to lie very still. He had few visitors, and his boredom was sublime. In his third week of hospitalisation he discovered himself thinking. His mind was operating almost outside himself, or rather, as he felt it, beside himself, and there was nothing he could do to control his thoughts and the dangerous path he knew they were treading. They had begun to question his very mode of existence. He wanted them very much to go away. But they were not visible visitors, and they were not restricted by any visitors' bell. They stayed by his reluctant side for the remainder of his hospital stay. When he came out, painfully and on crutches, he took a taxi back to his London flat, and for the first time it displeased him. He knew he could not live there much longer. He needed a change of address, he told himself, but when he questioned that need further, he knew it had nothing to do with premises. He eased himself into his leather armchair, and knew, that despite all his entrenched rationales, he could no longer live alone. That had been ten years ago. In the meantime, Wally had retired from his insurance job with a small pension and respectable savings, but he was still alone. He had tried. There were no doubt countless single women, who, in various drawing-rooms all over London and its suburbs, would loudly protest that they'd had their chances and some of them would surely have been Wally Peters. He had diligently done the rounds,

153

but no woman had obliged him. They preferred to catalogue him in their list of chances. Wally had come on the cruise in some desperation. He was conscious of the passing years. He had few friends and no family, and he didn't want to die without a mourner, an official one, whether she grieved or not. But he had to leave a legitimate memory, even if it was only of the marriage ceremony itself, or of the honeymoon, some event that he'd played a part in, some thought that he had shared. He looked at Mrs Dove. She'll forget me, he thought. As soon as the cruise is over. But if she married him, that would be something for her to remember and she could not recall it without some thought of himself. It was on the tip of his tongue to propose to her there and then, as she was sipping her coffee, and then he realised for the first time that he didn't know her Christian name. Everyone in their little group seemed to call her Mrs Dove. He could still hear Mr Bowers intoning it with the grave and peace that the name implied. Ellen and Alice Pickering did the same, and Mrs Dove's daughter, in his recollection, called her nothing, not even Mother. Did one have to know the name of one's intended in order to make a marriage proposal? After all, in many respects he knew her pretty well. He had held her hand on a Venice bench long enough to examine her unconscious face, to make leisurely acquaintance with each off-guard wart and superfluous hair, each wrinkle, each blackhead, each acne-ed pit. He had possibly viewed her at her very worst, a cheated view since she was unconscious of her display. Yet he still envisaged her as his bride and as his official mourner. And, in view of all that intimacy, was not her name a mere incidental?

She was still sipping her coffee, and he wondered how he could draw her attention. With the question he had in mind, he certainly could not call out: 'Mrs Dove.' And Wally had little talent for preamble, for warming to a subject, especially one which he felt already too hot to handle. 'Er...', he began.

She seemed not to hear him, so he poked her, gently, he thought, but not gently enough, for she spilled her coffee down her chin and looked at him with some annoyance. 'What on earth's the matter?' she said.

Even the insensitive Wally was sufficiently aware that this was no moment to press his suit. 'My hand slipped,' he said.

'I'm sorry. I was going to ask you something.' Though he knew it was ill-timed, he could not hold his hot tongue. At that moment he had her undivided attention. He couldn't be sure that such a moment would come again. 'I was thinking,' he said, 'well, it's like this, er … well I'm thinking of getting married.'

Mrs Dove put down her coffee cup. 'Oh that's nice,' she said, with faint feelings of rejection which for some reason did not upset her. 'Tell me about the lady. Does she live in London?'

Her reaction was unexpected. Wally assumed that she would identify herself with his intended. He did not quite know how to proceed. Then he decided to pick up on her question and turn it into a kind of game.

'Do you live in London?' he said.

'You know I don't,' Mrs Dove laughed. 'I live in Ilfracombe.'

'Oh well, the lady doesn't live in London then.' Wally thought he was being very subtle. And as he prided himself on his manoeuvre, Mrs Dove began to cotton on. She didn't know whether or not her conclusions pleased her, and she would have liked very much to change the subject so that she would have time to prepare herself for his next ploy.

'I don't know how anyone can live in London,' she said. 'It's such a dirty city.' She thought she had nicely skirted the matter in hand, but Wally picked up on that one too and said, 'She wouldn't have to live in London after the marriage.' Mrs Dove felt cornered. 'Oh that's nice,' she said again limply, and she didn't really know what she was talking about. She wished she had more coffee to busy herself with. She looked around for a waitress.

Now he had lost her attention. Moreover she was not playing his game. Or perhaps she didn't understand it. So much for subtlety, he thought. He decided to give it to her straight.

Mrs Dove managed to catch the eye of a waitress who crossed over to the table. She seemed to take an endless time filling her cup, and Wally grew impatient. He could not wait for the girl to go away.

'Would you marry me?' he shouted.

The waitress's hand trembled mid-air, and the coffee

slurped into the saucer. What with its absence of addressee, Wally's proposal might well have been directed towards her. She giggled, emptied the contents of the saucer back into the cup, and fled. The proposal still hung on the air. It was impossible to ignore. Its echo still reverberated, and, nameless as it was, it was clear to Mrs Dove that she would have to answer for it.

'Pardon?' she said, playing for time.

'Will you marry me?' he said again.

'We hardly know each other,' Mrs Dove tried. She didn't want to put him off altogether. But she needed time.

Wally laughed, and then went into details of how well he knew her, the bench they had shared in Venice, their tête-à-tête at the fancy dress ball. His voice grew louder with each detail of their close acquaintance. He was getting very cross indeed. Mrs Dove was embarrassed by possible eavesdroppers. His recital of her skin blemishes, even though he dressed it in what he considered to be affectionate laughter, was nonetheless very embarrassing when offered to the public ear.

'Oh sh...' she said, trying not to sound too harsh.

Then he lost his cool entirely. 'Well will you or won't you?' he screamed at her.

'Don't shout at me,' she whispered. 'I can't tell you straight away. I've got to think about it.'

'How long?' he said. He couldn't understand that his proposal needed any deliberation on her part. The woman was being ungrateful. He had it in mind to punish her. If they ever did get married, he'd make her pay for her hesitation.

'How long d'you want to think about it?' he said again. 'I'll leave you for a minute, and when you've finished your coffee, I'll come back,' he said.

She heard the threat in his voice. He moved away, upsetting one of the chairs in transit. Other passengers glanced in their direction. They were an unpleasantly noisy pair.

'I'll be back in a minute,' Wally said again.

A minute's too long, Mrs Dove thought, and a thousand years not long enough. She had made up her mind when he had first made his proposal clear. He was altogether an uncouth person, insensitive in the extreme, and possibly an expert bully. But she would marry him. He had offered her status, and that was all she would assent to. He had offered her a raison d'être to enter a supermarket and buy something a little more than a single lamb chop and a packet of frozen peas, and what's more, he would be footing the bill. He had offered her avenues of conversation on subjects other than her own ills and pains. She would refer to his, whatever they turned out to be, and if he had none, she would invent them. Above all, she would shed her widow's state. Her husband's death had angered her far more than it had grieved. It had been a far from happy marriage, and had served, in its twenty-five years duration, only to stock-pile the pains and hurts of Mrs Dove's secret and untouched arsenal. Even so, when he had died, she had felt ashamed of herself. She saw no difference between widowhood and spinsterhood. Both signified rejection, and rather than endure the embarrassment of living alone, she would marry anybody. Even Wally. Mrs Peters. She tried it on. Stella Peters. It would do. She knew that there were certain things she avoided thinking about. The hot dinner every day, the washing and the ironing, and the management of marriage silences. Above all she avoided thinking of the bed, but had to think of it first before putting it aside. She hoped that Wally was past all that filthy stuff, and would allow her her own quarters. The late Mr Dove at least had had the decency to do that, although she knew it was not for her sake but his own. His bedroom was at the far end of their huge Victorian barn of a house, and she knew that certain things went on there at night. She often heard strange voices, and usually they were not women's. She shut her eyes and shoved the pain aside. Stella Peters, she tried again. Mrs Peters, she tried over the telephone confirming her grocery order for two. She giggled with excitement. This is my husband, she tried out on her Ilfracombe circle. She was delaghted. The thought that the introduced husband would be Wally was not allowed to cross her mind. She looked up and saw him approaching the table, an irate schoolmaster come for the answer to a not too difficult question.

'Well?' he said, without bothering to sit down.

She did not look at him. He and his person had no relevence. 'Yes,' she said into her empty coffee-cup.

157

'Well that's alright then,' he said, sitting down heavily, and she had the impression that, had she said no, he would have hit her.

They looked at each other. 'It'll be alright, I know,' he said, and he wished to God he knew her name. He wondered how he could find out. Once the news of their betrothal was abroad, he could enquire of nobody. But he didn't worry too much about it. He knew that, if the worst came to the worst, he could peer over her shoulder while she was signing the register in the vestry. He was surprised at how little the news pleased him. He had expected, if not joy, then at least a great relief. But he felt neither. On the contrary. He was suddenly much afraid. He didn't know what people were supposed to do when they got married. He wasn't worried about the organisational side of it. That he could find in a reference book in any library. It was those other unthinkable things of which he'd never had experience. And he must never let on. She had to think that he knew everything. Otherwise she'd start getting ideas above her station. Moreover she would have to come and live in his place, whatever she thought of London. He wasn't going to traipse all the way to Ilfracombe. And what's more, he'd keep the flat in his name. Must start with a tight rein, he told himself. He began to dislike her a little. She had accepted his hand and, despite her plea for time to think it over, her acceptance had been with some alacrity. Her very acceptance of him marked her as being of little worth. But he did not consider withdrawing his proposal. Liking had nothing to do with marriage. They were about to sign a contract together, and it was of no matter whether the signatories were to each other's liking. He wondered whether all proposals were like this one and once again he wished for her name so that he could share with her some of his thoughts. But now, after the proposal, the appellation of Mrs Dove would have been contrary to form. He wondered how they would spend their time until their marriage. He dared not wonder further than that.

He needed her attention again. They had to talk of practicalities. He had to tell her of her move to London. He had to tell her what she could and could not expect. He wished he hadn't seen those warts on her face. But how, without name, to get her attention? She was looking into the far distance, and he imagined that she was dreaming herself into the bridal veil. So he shoved her. She came out of her reverie and she smiled at him. She touched his hands and he melted. He had made a good decision, he thought. It would not be too difficult to be kind to her. Then he was suddenly inspired. He'd read a book, a long time ago, for Wally was not a reading man, a love story, he remembered, and the hero's pet name for his beloved. He took Mrs Dove's hand. 'Honeybunch,' he said, his face wreathed with smiles, having found a solution to his problem.

'I like that name,' Mrs Dove said. 'It's so full of affection.'

'I mean it,' he said, and Mrs Dove thought that perhaps Wally wasn't so bad after all.

'Shall we tell the others?' she said, and by others, she meant the two widows, for it was in their ears that her triumph lay. She took care not to think of her daughter's reaction. It frightened her, and she wondered whether she should have asked Alice's permission before giving her hand so freely.

'What about your daughter?' Wally said, for it was her laughter he feared most of all.

'I think she should be pleased,' Mrs Dove dared to hope, 'as I would be, if she were to marry again.'

'She will, honeybunch,' Wally said. 'She's had a bad bashing, and you've got to give her time to get over it.'

He really is a very kind person, Mrs Dove thought, and dared to hope that in time he would give her daughter the love which she herself was incapable of showing.

'You tell them now, Wally,' Mrs Dove said timidly. 'They're all at the pool. You can tell them all together.'

He stood up and gave her his arm. He was nervous. He feared their stifled laughter, their barely concealed pity. Over the short distance between the dining-room and the pool, he would not have sufficient time to work himself up into a fever of contempt for all of them, which state would have helped him a little in countering their expected disdain. He marched Mrs Dove out of the dining-room, holding her a little before him, so that, if any blows were about to fall, she, like a hostage, would be in the direct line of fire, and would thus act for his protection.

The three women were sitting at the pool's edge, and Wally was glad that they were already assembled. He feared that

159

Mrs Dove would have shouted them out of the depths and lined them up to hear his amazing bulletin. He steered his intended towards the table. She stood there, shuffling, and quite clearly bursting with news.

'We're getting hitched,' Wally said suddenly, 'her and me.' He wasn't going to give them 'Honeybunch', and 'Mrs Dove' would no longer do.

Mrs Dove thought that hitched was a common word, and made her feel a little like a wagon. She giggled to cover her embarrassment.

'Hitched?' Ellen said. She genuinely had no idea what Wally Peters meant.

'I don't believe it,' Alice Dove said, though by her smile, she was prepared to be glad of it.

'Oh that's nice,' the other Alice said, and she felt very sorry for Mrs Dove. She hadn't realised how desperate she was.

Ellen didn't know what they were talking about, and she rather resented Alice for being so clever.

'Yes,' Mrs Dove said. 'We're getting married,' in a tone that she hoped was respectable and that put Ellen in the picture. Ellen was not pleased. Not that she had ever coveted Wally, but his intention reminded her of her own loss, and the possible future that Mr Bowers' death had denied her. She tried to smile and wish them well, but her heart was not in it. Alice shamed herself with her own thoughts. She was measuring Wally's possible dawn-performance with that of her own caller and she couldn't in any way make comparison. Her morning glory had nothing to do with marriage. Inside matrimony, it would have been shameful, disgusting and rude. It belonged to vice and to sin, and all beautiful things illegal. She turned her face from the table to hide her pleasure, for it had nothing to do with Wally's engagement.

Mrs Dove's Alice, on the other hand, displayed her pleasure unashamedly. Her mother was made to be partnered. She foundered in a single state, and her mother would look as a saviour upon anybody who could multiply it. Even such a one as Wally Peters who had so little to recommend him. She suspected that Wally too was incapable in his bachelorhood, and was seeking some multiple translator. And for him, too, anybody would fit the bill. With this grounding of compatibility, she could see no reason why it should not make the basis of a good partnership.

'Well we must celebrate,' Ellen said.

'You sound like poor Mr Bowers,' Mrs Dove whispered. 'It's such a shame. We would have invited him to our wedding, wouldn't we, Wally?'

There were other reasons for Mr Bowers to live, Ellen thought, and Wally Peters' nuptials were the least of them. She grew deeply resentful.

'It's too early to drink,' Wally was saying, and Ellen knew that Mr Bowers would have crooned champagne, whatever the hour. Mean man, she thought, that Wally.

'We'll celebrate this evening,' he said. 'All of us. At dinner. I'll buy us champagne.'

Ellen bit her lip. That man was not allowed to have anything in common with Mr Bowers.

'Where are you going to live?' Alice asked her mother, and Mrs Dove realised that they hadn't discussed any practicalities, and she wondered whether she had given her answer too quickly, an answer to which no conditions were attached. She had no intention of moving from Ilfracombe. All her friends were there, and the major bonus of her re-marriage was its proud and continuous publication. 'In London of course.' Wally said. In his mind there had never been any alternative.

Mrs Dove swallowed. He was clearly not open to argument. She wished they were alone, so that she might try to dissuade him. Later on perhaps, she thought, when the ladies would go into the pool, she could outline to him the benefits of ozone in Ilfracombe. But she was fearful even of its suggestion. He might withdraw his proposal altogether. 'But we'll be married in Ilfracombe,' she said, half questioning.

'Of course,' Wally said largely. 'The bride's home town.' He had no particular group of friends to invite in London. Anyway a provincial wedding would undoubtedly be cheaper. Mrs Dove was happy to settle for an Ilfracombe ceremony. Once was enough to let people know. She wished the ladies would get into the pool. She had so many questions to ask her future husband. She wanted a description of his house. She assumed without question that it was a house; the term 'flat' would have horrified her. It held provincial overtones of poverty. She wanted to know the number of its rooms, especially bedrooms, though she feared his detailed answer to that one. Was there a garden, and what was she supposed to do with all her furniture? And the photograph of Mr Dove on her bedside table? Would that be allowed, she wondered, and if not in Wally's house, where could she put it? Alice might be prepared to give it house-room, but no more than that. No occasional look of regret or remembrance of any kind. She would shove it under her books, having extracted it from its silver frame. Or would boiler-suited Nellie replace him? That thought upset Mrs Dove profoundly. She would hide Mr Dove in his silver lining in the bottom of her suitcase, and look at him from time to time and realise that she'd made the same mistake all over again. She tried not to think of the folly of her intent, of leaving her home town, where she'd been born and been showed off and showed off her own in her turn, her small circle of friends who still respected her husband's memory, conned by the lie of their public marriage-face. She had habituated herself to their deception and had lived contentedly within it, conning herself in the process. and this she would leave, the lie of it, in exchange for another, a new falsehood that would take longer to spread abroad, and even longer for convincing self-deception. I'm Mrs Stella Peters, she kept saying to herself, and this is my husband, Wally. Her renewed status comforted her a little, and she wondered what she should wear for her Ilfracombe wedding.

'When is it to be?' her daughter said.

Her mother looked at Wally for his date-permission. Wally hesitated, and not between a choice of dates. He had proposed. She had accepted. That, in his mind, was all there was to it. He realised, for the first time, that he didn't really want to marry. The idea terrified him. He could only pursue, make an offer, and if accepted, run for his life. He was capable only of dress-rehearsal, and that small run-through with Mrs Dove as his partner was now well and truly over. He looked at his intended and she at him, and it was clear that both found each other faintly resistible. But words had been spoken, they both knew, words that pointed to a deed, and that deed must now be done and seen to be done. 'After the cruise,' Wally said. Such a timing left the whole business vaguely open.

After the cruise could be in their dotage, when neither of them would be fit enough to make the church.

'Yes, but when?' Alice Dove insisted, sniffing a faint odour of retreat.

'Well it will take quite a time to arrange things, won't it Wally?' Mrs Dove said, allowing him some leeway. She didn't want him to feel pushed into marriage. Yet he had asked her, and had announced it publicly, so he had to keep his word. Sooner or later. But she would not give him too long. 'In about a month?' she asked.

That should be long enough, he thought, to lose sight of her, to seek out another, to propose, to be accepted, and once again to run for his life. 'A month is fine,' he said. He wouldn't even have to go to the trouble of finding out her name. Honeybunch would do till the end of the cruise. And on no account would he divulge his London address, neither would he press for hers, and they need never cross each other's paths again. He felt profoundly relieved, and he smiled at her.

'Well I'm going for a swim,' Alice Dove said. She was not entirely confident in his vagueness, and she thought the two of them should be left alone to discuss their marriage plans in greater particular. 'Are you coming?' she said to Ellen and Alice.

They both got up and shed their towels. Alice Dove swam to the far end of the pool, and there she hung on to the rail wondering whether to advise her mother against the folly she was about to commit. The Pickering Alice went into the pool to float upon the water to dream of her dawn-caller and to cool off the ardour that his morning-absence had fed. Ellen went into the pool to cry.

Now Wally and Mrs Dove were left alone, and Wally was very nervous indeed. He was conscious of ten more days in which to play the groom-elect, and if he were to play that role, even if he knew how, it would be caddish behaviour indeed. Wally was an insensitive man, but he was by no means malicious. He did not want to upset Mrs Dove, whatever her name was. He hoped to get by for ten days with a smile. This he now gave her, so wide and so fixed that it was slightly unnerving.

'Where do you live in London?' Mrs Dove dared.

'In Battersea,' he lied, and he congratulated himself on the alacrity of his fabrication. He had been to Battersea once to visit a client. He did not like the area. He always felt uneasy on the south side of the Thames. He lived in Camden Town, always had done, and he looked upon a journey across the river as some kind of safari.

'Is it nice there?' she said.

He decided to paint for her a beautiful Battersea picture. He wanted to leave her with at least one happy memory. 'It's a lovely area,' he said. 'My house overlooks the river.' He decided to make it a house. He had heard of the provincial flat prejudice. 'At night I stand on the patio,' he went on shamelessly, delighting in his detailed architectural conversions, 'and I listen to the ships' hooters, and watch their lights glitter on the water.' He took care not to mention the belching smoke from the Battersea power station. Mrs Dove's eyes were alight with the romance of it all. Only once in her life had she been to London and she did not recall the visit with any pleasure. It had been Mr Dove's idea for their honeymoon. He'd been there once himself to a football match, and on the basis of his knowledge of Fulham football ground and two or three bars near Piccadilly Circus, he considered he knew London like the back of his hand and was intent on proving it to his young bride. They had spent two days getting lost in the great metropolis, and never once would he ask the way. For he knew it, he said. He didn't need direction. After their first foray to Buckingham Palace, which they never reached, her feet blistered and altogether London-weary, she had dared to suggest a guided bus tour. It was then that she first suspected his capacity for violence. He didn't actually hit her, but it was terrifyingly close. He'd raised his hand, which hovered, then he scratched his head. But she knew his head was not itching. She hated London, and Buckingham Palace in particular, and that made her uncomfortable, because she had been brought up to love the monarchy who were unthinkable without reference to their address. 'Is Battersea near Buckingham Palace?' she asked.

'Very close,' Wally said. 'I'll take you there.'

His answer pleased her beyond measure. It would give her a chance to restore her faith in the monarchy, and learn to love the Queen once more.

164

'How many rooms in your house?' she grew more bold.

Wally decided to go the whole way. He recalled the house advertisements he'd read in the papers for Sunday diversion, and rattled them off with the occasional authenticating hesitation. 'It has four bedrooms,' he said, 'and two bathrooms. One en-suite.' She raised her eyebrows. 'That means one bathroom leads off the main bedroom.' My God, she is stupid, he thought. 'Then it has two reception rooms,' he plodded on, 'and a morning-room which is drenched in morning sunlight' – he was happy to remember that promotional phrase. 'And a kitchen, and of course a utility room. For the washing and drying machines,' he added assuming that she was as ignorant of utilities as she was of en-suite. He watched her eyes widen with delight, and he felt a swine and rather enjoyed it. He gave a fond thought to his little bed-sitter in Camden Town which those same advertisements now described as a studio flat, and that pleased him because it made him think he was an artist.

'Why d'you have such a large house if you're on your own?' Mrs Dove asked with eminent logic.

Wally hesitated. He hadn't meant his fictitious house to be a subject of prolonged conversation. 'I like big places,' he said. 'Friends come and stay sometimes.'

Mrs Dove was very excited at the prospect of London house parties. She'd read about them in magazines at the hairdressers. 'What about my furniture?' she said. She was getting very bold now.

Wally shifted with apprehension. The vision of a removal van outside her Ilfracombe premises terrified him. It was all going too far and too quickly. The transfer of furniture was a very serious proposition. He could not even allow for its discussion. She might well sue him for breach of promise. He bitterly regretted having announced his false intentions to the other ladies who would lie on her behalf like eye-witnesses. 'We'll see,' he temporised, and smiled again, hoping that that would satisfy her.

Mrs Dove knew when not to push her luck. She had gleaned sufficient and satisfactory information for one session. The small matter of the furniture could be held in abeyance and, if necessary, shelved entirely. She would miss her mahogany sideboard though. Perhaps it could find a home in

165

what he called the utility room. She couldn't wait to get back to Ilfracombe and describe her new home to her friends. She gave him back his smile, and both knew that that signified the end of the conversation.

'Honeybunch,' he said. It was his devious Amen.

The women emerged from the pool. They now felt very much a threesome, and were bent on leaving what Alice Dove called the love-birds, to themselves to sort out their future. The Pickering Alice was intent to get back to her cabin and stay there all day in case her caller decided to make up for his dawn's absence. Ellen, too, wanted to return to her cabin, but with no such joyful expectation. She would sit on her bed, and hold the eight-pronged knife in her hand, and realise how futile was its purpose and its purchase. Alice Dove declared she was going to the ship's library to write some letters and her mother prayed that Nellie was not the addressee. But she needn't have worried. Her Alice did not have Nellie in mind as a correspondent. She would pick up on an old boy-friend she'd known before her marriage. One especially she remembered with more than affection. David Wiles. His name and his full London address flashed through her mind with exhilarating clarity. She almost skipped to the writing-room.

As she reached the door, the waiter crossed her path. Unlike her namesake and Ellen, Alice Dove had no cause to avoid him or to seek him out. He smiled at her. 'The Campari lady,' he said.

She was pleased with his smile and his observance. 'I think I'll have one now, to celebrate,' she said.

'May I ask what you're celebrating, Madame?' The waiter knew his place and his mien, and was careful not to outstep either. She sniffed his plebeian brilliantine smell, and knew that all his life he would be a waiter.

'My mother's getting married,' she said. 'To Wally. Wally Peters.'

'Congratulations,' he said. Mating was in the air. He looked her over. He knew from hearsay the story of her Venice baptism. He knew from eavesdropping of her man-hatred. He knew, from his first dirty-dungareed sight of her, what kind of woman she was, and he knew above all exactly what she bloody well needed. And had probably never had.

And he knew in his mind that he was the one to give it to her.

'I'll bring your drink to the library,' he said. He made his way to the bar and tried not to think about her. The risk would be great, but her imagined resistance was sublime. In the long years of his career as waiter/raper, he had never before encountered such a challenge. If he could get away with her, he would regard it as the peak of his career. He might even think of retiring. But he knew such thoughts were folly. One couldn't retire from appetite, and as long as it raged within him, he must confine it to the high seas where detection ran less of a risk, for a cruise was fantasy-land and, in all aspects, unreal. Yes, he thought, he might well give her a try.

That night, he idled a while on deck, and saw the two lovebirds strolling along the rail. Occasionally they stopped and looked into the water. He wondered why they were not arm-in-arm and why they seemed to have so little to say to each other. In their presence at the rail, he knew that the coast in Mrs Dove's cabin was clear. He knew the time to be opportune. But he mistrusted his impetuosity. Once before on a cruise some years ago, the same route as this one, he recalled, his rashness had almost put an end to his raping and waiting vocation. It had taught him never to act on impulse again. No, he would bide his time, and in the meantime, make do with the other one. He turned to make his lustful way to her cabin, but noted her, still abroad, on the other side of the deck. She was with her friend, the morning-chiffoned number whom he knew was going to miss him terribly. He leaned against the post, and waited for them to turn in, feeding his appetite on thoughts of the dungareed one, whom he had heard hated men to distraction.

Ellen and Alice walked arm-in-arm, glad of each other's comfort. Alice was content to listen to Ellen talk about Mr Bowers, and her sadness at his passing. Again Ellen was tempted to confide in Alice, such was the gentle trust presently between them, and she might well have done so had she not known that there was little that Alice could do about it. She was tempted too to tell her the truth of Mr Bowers' marriage. She wanted to convince her friend of the intimacy that had grown between them. That story would have confirmed it in Alice's mind. But Ellen decided to forego that card. Its playing would have been too costly to Mr Bowers' memory.

'Look,' Alice said suddenly.

They stopped at the rail and leaned over. A lantern moved slowly along the water. On closer inspection, they saw that it was attached to a small boat, and in that boat lay a long box. The splutter of an engine apologised for its disturbance of the night, and the silhouette of two crew-men swayed in the ship's light. The women watched. 'They're going to bury him in Limassol,' Alice said. 'I'm glad we saw his funeral.'

Ellen started to weep. It was such a desolate, lonely end. Alone on the black water with strangers by his side, bound for a hole in an alien ground, which site no-one would ever know or care to discover. With no-one to mourn him, no-one to question autopsy, no-one to express surprise. Above all, no single person who knew the truth of him. Except herself. He had left an onerous legacy, and she shivered with the responsibility of it all.

'He's gone to join his wife,' Alice said. 'We must look on the bright side of things.'

But Ellen knew that there would be nothing bright about that possible reunion.

The two women embraced each other and said goodnight. Alice moved away, leaving Ellen staring across the water. The waiter watched her. For a moment he pitied her. But remorse must never interfere with his business. She turned from the rail, and so did he, and followed her to her cabin.

CHAPTER TEN

A salutary lesson

In their separate cabins, the late Mr Bowers' party were reading that section of the cruise-brochure relating to the visit to Limassol. The most recurrent word in the short paragraph was 'romance' which was promised in every line. A wine festival would take care of the morning, during which the promise of romance would be seriously considered. At the afternoon's flower festival, that same promise would be declared, and the evening's stroll along the beaches would be the time and place for its fulfillment. Both Ellen and Alice found the whole day faintly resistible. For Alice, all romance, whether considered, declared or fulfilled, lay in her cabin in the early hours of the day. Outside that time and place, there was an interval elsewhere that had to be filled with some innocuous occupation. She would have happily stayed on board all day. As for Ellen, the promise of romance in Limassol was a cruel joke that fate had played her. That promise had sailed away in a long black box, beyond declaration, beyond fulfillment. The wine and flower festivals, the stroll on the beaches, could only be a reminder of what she had lost. Once more she counted the days to her return. Interminable they seemed. Ten days of dread, ten nights of terror. She wondered whether she would ever recover.

In his cabin, Wally Peters read his brochure, and its promise of romance unnerved him. He knew it was up to the man to make those promises, that it was man's work to manufacture romance, that women were only on the receiving end. He felt suddenly very responsible, as if the brochure were giving him orders, reminding him of work to be done in his department. The wine and flower festivals did not over-worry him; others would take care of that organised enjoyment. It was the beach-strolling that bothered him, an unorganised pursuit, in which he would be expected to run the show. He knew what was expected of him. He'd seen it in magazines. The sea-shore was a favourite venue for lovers, and usually at night. They were known to stroll hand-in-hand at the water's edge, and in time they would kiss, and in more time, do other things that Wally tried not to think about. He did not want to kiss Mrs Dove. The thought repelled him. Yet, as his intended, or so she thought, she had a right to expect it. She wouldn't be satisfied with the occasional hand-hold and the monotonous repetition of 'Honeybunch'. Suddenly he was inspired. He would not lay a finger on her, pleading for his virginity, a woman's prerogative, he knew, but he'd borrow it for the time. No, he would keep his hands to himself, and cherish and value her honour until they were duly wed. He was mightily pleased with his idea.

Of all their little party, only Mrs Dove and her daughter looked forward with excitement to their day in Limassol. And both for different reasons. Alice Dove was available to every new experience, no matter how trivial. Since her Venetian rejuvenation, she had become a child of feverish curiosity. She had never been to either a wine or flower festival, and she would record it with a child's eye, and with that same eye, remember it.

Unlike her daughter, Mrs Dove was less interested in wine and flowers, which were the affairs of a crowd, than in the beach strolling which was a clear act of privacy. Along the sea-shore, she hoped to hear from her suitor the practicalities of his intentions. There was the question of honeymoon, summer holidays, the number and quality of his friends. Did he eat a cooked breakfast, and would he bring her tea in bed? Her own bed, she dared to hope, which he could well afford in that house of his. Above all, she wanted to know about money, and what she could expect by way of financial settlement and support. But these were questions she knew she would not ask, especially strolling along a moon-lit beach. She could only hope that Wally would be forthcoming, and would lay his fiscal cards on the table. 'D'you think Wally will make a good husband?' she asked her daughter, and then regretted it in case the answer was negative and she would have to act upon it.

'If you want him, of course he will,' Alice said. 'He seems a good enough man. But you must be sure of yourself,' she added, astonishing herself with the intimacy. She had never spoken of personal matters to her mother, nor she to her, and what she had said had been personal indeed, for it pointed to a skill of self-awareness that her mother had never known. All her life her mother had depended on other people to make her decisions. The notion of the need to know what one wanted had never been a viable proposition. Her father had insinuated himself into Mrs Dove's affections because he had told her that she needed him. She had believed him, and possibly still did, despite the years of battering misery. She believed herself to be at fault. There could be no other explanation. And it would be the same with Wally, Alice feared. 'What d'you want?' she said suddenly. 'D'you want to be married, or d'you want to be married to Wally?'

'That's a silly question,' her mother parried, knowing that it was not silly at all. That it struck at the very root of her dilemma, which she herself had not even acknowledged as a quandary. 'I want to marry Wally,' she said, and she thought it sounded quite ridiculous.

'Then he'll make you a good husband,' Alice said. And without forethought, which would have restrained her, she went over to where her mother was sitting and put her arms around her.

Mrs Dove did not know what to do with the embrace. It had been years since anyone had held her, and it frightened her. She thought she might erupt like a long-dormant volcano, and her lava would rage with longing. She feared she might explode, not into pieces of manageable proportions, one piece for her anger, one for her frustration, and a boulder for her value unsung. No, she would explode into a million splintered fractions, all bloody, and all terrible to view. She sat rigid in Alice's arms, shivering with her fear, yet with a small area of awareness of how beautiful it all was. Why do I need to marry Wally? she dared ask herself. The question marked her first step into adulthood. She did not take it warily. She was not conscious of taking it at all. Her daughter's embrace had jettisoned her into a state of fearful self-awareness, of sudden questionings, of confirmation, perhaps, that after all the rigid, frigid years, she might be, oh

171

please God, touchable. Such a presumptuous thought had never crossed her mind, but Alice's embrace had prompted it, had freed such a confrontation. Mrs Dove shivered in her daughter's arms, and knew that she had changed and could never be the same again.

Alice continued to hold her. For her too, it was a moment of revelation. A moment to prolong and try to understand. She marvelled at the miraculous speed of the change in her filial feelings. A million words between them, and as many days, could never have achieved such change. For words, however strong, however moving, clever or sincere were postponements, weapons against the nudge of one's consciousness, against the audacity of insight. A simple touch, flesh on flesh, could conquer all. An embrace could, in a second, tear down the barriers that over the years had been structured with such innocent and such corrosive skill. It took another kind of art to embrace, and a kind of courage too, and timing was all. The miracle that had occurred in that cabin was, all of it, timing. She moved away, leaving her arm prints on her mother's body. 'I'll see you on deck,' Alice said, and Mrs Dove was glad to be left alone for a while to put her new-found strength to some purpose. To decide what to do with Wally.

There was now no question in her mind that she would marry him. It was impossible. She confessed to herself for the first time, that only the status of marriage appealed to her, that Wally could give her nothing that she needed, that he could not touch her with anything but formality. It was loving she needed, caring and concern, and those, in her experience, did not necessarily have to do with marriage. But they were available, she knew, and she now knew too, with absolute certainty, that she was available to them. Wally was peripheral, a cruise-companion, no more, who would be forgotten before she reached Ilfracombe. But how to tell him? How to disengage herself from his London home, from his four bedrooms and the bathroom that was part of one of them. She did not want to hurt him. She would sooner play him along than watch him suffer her rejection. With her new confidence, she had acquired cunning, a trait unknown to her hitherto. She decided to pretend that no change had occurred in her heart. But she would not give him her address and, if pressed, would give a false one. She would leave him with no means of communication. She would bid him a fond farewell on the dockside, with promises to get in touch. If she remembered him at all, she knew it would be with an affectionate shudder. She prepared herself for their day's outing, and left the cabin.

Mr Bowers' little party, as they were still known to the ship's passengers despite their present lack of leadership, assembled together on the deck. There was a nervousness about all of them, and each wondered at the other's lack of spirit, and they ascribed it to a lingering mourning for poor Mr Bowers. Mr Bowers' demise was coming in very handy. It was a convenient explanation for all waywardness and lack of countenance. None of them would have offered it as an excuse, though each hoped the others would take it into consideration.

They leaned over the rail, watching the ship manoeuvre itself along the jetty. Then the gangway was secured and the passengers disembarked. Alice Dove took her mother's arm while Wally was looking for it. When he saw it occupied, he feigned disappointment, and took Ellen's arm as a substitute. Ellen was totally indifferent as to how she was helped down the gangway, or whether indeed she disembarked at all. Alice Pickering brought up the rear alone, though feeling no need for company. She looked back at the ship's rail, in the hope of catching sight of her suitor, so that the print of his image could remain in her eye for the whole day. But amongst other waiters, who stood there, he was nowhere to be seen.

The courier was waiting at the bottom of the steps. He eyed Mr Bowers' party with apprehension. He hoped they were not going to give any trouble. A bus was waiting to take them to the centre of the town, and he urged the passengers to take their seats, though most of them were hardly off the boat. Ellen was the first to board, on Wally's arm. The bus appeared empty, but there was a smell of occupation. A brilliantine smell. Ellen peered into the darkness and deciphered him sitting on the back seat. She hesitated, but Wally urged her forward and there was nothing she could do but board. Quickly she took the front seat, a single one on the edge of the doors. Wally sat behind her assuming that she was freeing him for Mrs Dove's company and he was not grateful for her sensitivity. Ellen sat motionless, wondering what he was doing there.

'Hullo there,' she heard Wally say, and he could only have been addressing the brilliantine since there was no-one else on the bus. 'You coming along with us?'

'That's right,' he said. 'Some friends in Limassol.'

Mrs Dove and her Alice were next on the bus. Alice relinquished her mother's arm and sat on the seat opposite Ellen's, also a single one, and Mrs Dove had no choice but to place herself next to her never-intended. He smiled at her, taking her arm, his public gesture. Then Alice, the other one, boarded. 'Why don't you come and sit with me?' she said, seeing Ellen on her own.

But Ellen didn't want to rise and turn around and catch sight of him again. 'I like to be by the door, for air,' she said, and looking, she saw Alice turn very pale. 'You look as if you could do with some air yourself,' Ellen said.

Alice had smelled him too, then followed her nose to its source. He looked different without his white steward's coat, without a drinks-tray or any insignia of his calling. He could have been anybody sitting there, and the lack of recognition, as Alice caught his eye, confirmed him as a stranger. It even crossed her mind to go and sit next to him and strike up a conversation. But she thought better of it. She was ruffled by his presence, his trayless, bedless presence. Somehow she could not place him, but she knew by the tremblings in her body that he was no stranger. She sat behind her namesake and let her blushings subside.

The bus was filling up. Ellen heard other people acknowledge the waiter, and after a while, she dared to steal a glance behind her to discover his seating companion. But he remained alone, as if the passengers acknowledged his calling and allowed him to know his place. Ellen looked out of the window trying to produce some excitement in herself at the sight of such unaccustomed scenery. There was no question of its splendour. She itemised everything she saw, the blue sea on the one side, and the cypress-lined avenue on the other. She noted the colours, at least six different shades of green in the landscape, the rainbows of bougainvillea, the countless blues in the sky. She knew that it was beautiful. But it did not disturb the nerve of her eye, did not stir any part of her body

174

with delight. She knew the reason for her paralysed lack of response. It was sitting not far behind her, and she writhed with deep resentment that he had spoiled her pleasure. There was poor Mr Bowers too, but somehow the sadness of his passing was now less painful. Having seen him laid to rest, or at least on his way to a resting-place, she had been able to place him in the past, and thus allow time to heal. As she sat there looking out of the window at the beauty that did not register, she was surprised at how little Mr Bowers had to do with her depression. She missed him. She would have been glad of his company. But she no longer ached for him. But for his secret, she would no doubt in time have forgotten him. It was his final gift to her, and that alone assured him a place in her memory. No it was not Mr Bowers' death that blurred the cypresses or registered the colours like a cold kaleidoscope. It was the terror of her nights that had paralysed her eye, and she could have killed him just for that, not for his assault, not for the cold fear he instilled, but simply because he had numbed her heart. She was startled that the fear of his nightly visits was secondary, that the terror was diluting, that she was slowly habituating herself to his nightly alarm. She counted the nights again. She counted them in the cypresses she saw without seeing. She ticked off ten of their number and turned her face from the window. For a moment she decided that she would shelve her revenge, spend no more time planning his retribution, and simply put up with it until the cruise was all over. The thought disturbed her, that her body could so accustom itself to its assault that it would come almost to expect it as its due. She dared to think about his performance, and knew that that too had become a habit. Every move was predictable, even its timing. She recapped on the stages of his act, his entrance, his business, his photographic display, and his silent leavetaking, a path of solid brilliantine in his wake. He seemed almost bored with it all, as if it were an exercise he was obliged to perform each night before going to bed, and it was her bad luck that her cabin happened to be his gymnasium. That thought drew her anger again, and sprouted her feelings of revenge. She wished she had her knife about her. Now she could do it, rushing to the back of the bus, and in front of all the passengers, fan his filthy body with her blades. They would think she'd gone

175

mad, that the target of her rage held no relevance, that she had blown without rhyme or reason. And she would not have denied it. She would have been glad to be thought mad in such a cause.

They were approaching the junction of a cross-road, and the bus slowed down and drew in at the kerb. On the sidewalk was an open-air café overhung with vines and the centre of bustling activity. A group of dancers in national costume was performing around the bus-stop by way of a welcoming committee. One woman, with two children at her side, was scanning the faces in the bus windows in happy expectation.

'There she is,' the bus-driver called out, and as if in answer to a summons, the waiter bounded down the centre of the bus. He was the first to alight. 'Regards to your wife,' the bus-driver shouted after him.

The news of his marital status was a matter of indifference to all but two passengers. Alice bridled with jealousy. She had never envisaged her dawn-caller in a marriage context. His performance was that of a freak, a sport, totally outside conventional partnership. Yet there under her nose was evidence that, in some area at least, he was exactly like Pickering, with two children like her own, but unlike hers, unnaturally born, spawned from his hissing vocabulary. Out of his filthy lexicon he had fashioned two human forms. She stared at them for some sign of abnormality, but they reminded her of her own, so many years ago, and, watching him embrace his wife, she feared that he would never come to her again.

The passengers started to alight. All but Ellen who remained seated knowing that now was her chance, knowing that this was the moment for his exposure. She didn't know how she would do it except that it would be away from the public eye, as privately as was possible in such a communal gathering. She waited for all the passengers to alight. Alice hung back waiting for her, then shrugged and followed the Doves and Wally into the café. The waiter and his family were still at the bus-stop, the woman chattering and laughing with news of home in his absence. Ellen watched all the passengers into the café and out of sight and then she alighted, and, without any plan or forethought, she strode to

176

the woman and gripped her arm. The woman looked at her, bewildered, and then at her husband for some explanation. And Ellen gave it to her, loud, angry and clear, and in a language that was totally unintelligible.

'Your husband,' she hissed, 'is a rapist.' That for openers. She paused to let it sink in. The waiter smiled, and his wife took her cue from him, as did the children who probably thought the foreign lady was mad. 'Every night he comes to my cabin and does terrible things to me,' Ellen raved on, as yet unaware that only the waiter knew what she was talking about. Then he laughed aloud and so did his wife, and she laughed again when her husband mistranslated Ellen's out-pourings. His wife responded with a jumble of words, and the waiter translated for Ellen. 'My wife says she is glad you like her country.' Then they laughed again, harmoniously, as a family, and Ellen turned away, wishing for her knife which, at that moment, she could have wielded with little compunction.

She made her way towards the café where Wally and his ladies were already wine-sampling. They looked a gay crowd, and Ellen stood on the threshold rubbing her face as if to wipe away her rage. She wanted to join in their merry-making; she wanted to drink herself into oblivion, to be carried back to her cabin, and there sleep undisturbed until their return to Southampton. As soon as I'm home, I shall forget all about it, she told herself. All she would remember was that she had come out of it alive, and slowly she would turn that into an advantage and perhaps even celebrate it. In time, she might even tell Alice, knowing that Alice was too innocent to believe her. She felt a deep affection for her friend, and thought that next summer they might spend together in a boarding house at an English seaside.

'Come along Ellen,' Wally shouted across the café.

She joined them at their table. The wine had been recently bottled and had the rough edge of new vintage. None of the party liked the taste of it, but it would have seemed offensive to their hosts to leave it undrunk. After two glasses, the taste-buds were numbed. It became drinkable and would do its inebriating duty. Wally was already well beyond the threshold, and so was Mrs Dove, and together they discussed their marriage plans with eager excitement, each containing a

177

small area of sobriety which spelt out their mutual deception. Mrs Dove had declared what she was going to wear for her wedding, and her daughter had offered to do the catering. They even went into details as to the menu. Wally's contribution was his honeymoon suggestion, a week in New York to see the sky-scrapers, and at that promise, Mrs Dove's resolve was slightly shaken. She would have loved to go to America, even if it had to be with Wally and at the cost of the Wally-price she would have to pay for the rest of her life. Then she recalled her daughter's embrace, and at that moment Alice touched her mother's arm, and all was well again with her resolve. And assured now of the deception, she declared that she would give a supper-party to her out-of-town guests on the eve of her wedding. This last to Ellen and Alice, who agreed to travel up the day before and splash out on an Ilfracombe hotel. The prospect of such festivities which sounded in Ellen's ear so genuine gave her some expectation of the future. With the wine's help the waiter was already a blurred image in her mind. In time his story would be tellable, as a myth, an unfairy tale over the garden wall, and Alice would boggle at her friend's imagination, and even Ellen would wonder where she got it all from.

Two accordion-players approached their table in invitation to the dancing which was already well under way on the café square. Ellen felt very much like dancing and looked around hopefully for a partner. A man caught her eye, not one of the passengers, she registered, for he was wearing national costume. He approached the table and gave Ellen his arm. She took it straightaway and followed him into the square. He clearly had no language for her, just his smiles and his guidance. Ellen wanted nothing more, and as he danced her over the flagstones, she noted the face of a passing dancer, his arm around a woman and two children, and she wondered why his face was vaguely familiar. The blur of his image inspired her to a new method of accommodating the nightly visitor, now a dark shadow without the substance of fear and terror. Every night before going to bed, she would drink herself into her present undeciphering state. Then she would only half know what was happening and her fears and disgust would be diluted too. She would explain to Alice that she had acquired a taste for wine at the wine festival and the story could hold for the rest of the cruise. She gripped her partner's hand with affection as if it were he who had inspired her partial solution. She vaguely saw Alice sail by on the arm of another native, and Alice Dove, too, was similarly partnered. She looked back at their table and saw the two lovebirds alone and wondered why they were not talking to each other.

Wally missed the company and so did Mrs Dove. For some reason it seemed easier to deceive in the presence of an audience. The lie face-to-face threatened more serious consequences than that which was publicly declared. There was a greater immorality in the private falsehood that, to an audience, could pass as a show, a comedy perhaps, a performance on which the curtain would eventually come down and reality be restored.

'Would you like to dance?' Wally said, wishing to escape their privacy. And for the same reason Mrs Dove obliged and he drove her onto the square.

The courier stood on the sidelines timing the passenger's enjoyment. The flower-parade would start within the hour and was held in the town-centre. He had to reckon on the bus journey and the time to herd them altogether. He cast a special eye on Wally Peters who seemed to have taken over the leadership of that difficult party and he was relieved to see that so far they were all behaving themselves. He would allow them one more dance before herding them on their way to their second organised pleasure.

When the dance finished, the band and the dancers returned to the serious business of wine-tasting, so that when the courier gave the signal to depart, his flock was barely ambulatory. He did what he could to get them onto the bus, but it took time and persuasion. He was deeply ashamed of his charges. Though in the pleasure business, his own pleasure was not part of his trade. It was something he organised for others, and it would have seemed to be short-changing to take a little of it for himself. He was glad that the flower-parade was a sedentary affair, a situation that would excercise some control on his clients' frivolity.

Ellen and Alice looked around the bus, and both for the same reason. But he had not resumed his seat. For a moment Ellen allowed herself the hope that he would remain with his family in Limassol and not rejoin the ship that night, and Alice had the same fleeting thought and feared it.

They were nearing the centre of the town. A raised stand of benches lined the streets. Most of the seats were already occupied with an expectant crowd. The whole of the front row on one side was empty, and loudly translated the brochure's promise of V.I.P. treatment for its guests. The bus came to a stop at the side of the square. There was little time before the parade started and the courier was anxious to get them seated. The passengers were not disposed to move yet again and they left their seats reluctantly and in no particular order. Groups were separated, and passengers found themselves in the front row seats next to faces they had vaguely seen aboard ship but who were strangers to them. Wally found himself alone and was not displeased with his placing. Alone was the safest way to be, with all the lies he had to fabricate in company. He looked down the line. He skimmed over Mrs Dove who was in rapt conversation with her neighbour, the crochet-lady as she was known on the ship, old in years and fragile, who spent most of her time in a deck-chair plying her needle and yarn in a frail filigree, a delicate tracery that matched the languor of her years. Further along the line he saw Alice Dove, who was trapped between the bus-driver and the courier who looked as if they were keeping a wary eye on her. Ellen was further down the line amply neighboured by rowdy passengers, but she took no part in their revelries. She might as well have been on her own. Strange woman, that Ellen, Wally thought. Had a mind of her own. Always dangerous in a woman, he had heard, and believed it too, for his own security. He was glad he hadn't courted her. She would have rejected him, he knew. She still had the audacity to be choosey, and at her age too. He threw her a look of contempt. Then there was her friend Alice, the quiet one, sitting almost on the end of the line. She was smiling to herself as she always seemed to be, with a look of blissful beatitude that sometimes got on his nerves. He was glad he was alone. He wouldn't come on a cruise again, he decided. It offered too little scope. He would go to a Butlins' camp, where the canvas was larger and of more infinite variety.

He could see the floats lining up at the end of the square.

He shuffled his feet with excitement. He loved parades. His father, a shadowy figure in his childhood, had been a regular soldier, and on his occasional leaves, he would instruct his son in the art of marching as if it were a skill that required much intelligence and application. Wally thought his father owned the army, and the power to do with it what he willed. So he never understood why one day he was killed and, almost the next, so it seemed to him at the time, there was another soldier in the house who pretended to be his father. He heard the stirrings of a band and saw the marching drums and pipes and Wally was a child again, grinning from ear to ear and his neighbours on the stand wondered why he was standing and jumping on his little feet. They had always thought that that Wally man was a bit simple and now they knew it for sure. The people behind him shouted at him to sit down, and he turned and sulked at them, but obeyed, and sat quietly with his hands folded in his lap as his mother had taught him. Yet still his little feet beat time to the band as he was shipped back into his childhood. His body trembled with patriotic fervour that was in no way diluted by the foreign soil on which he stood.

Mrs Dove was watching the floats, and thinking of her own Ilfracombe garden. She wondered how she could ever have thought of giving it up. She suddenly missed it and the pleasure it promised her, her preparations for each season, her morning walk along the flower borders. She looked down the line at her innocent rejectee and saw him tapping his little feet on the ground. For a moment she was sorry for him, but then she thought that he was really rather childish and silly.

Ellen tried to find some pleasure in the flower-parade. Her own garden at home was full of roses. Walsh had been a rose man. His leisure time was spent between his roses in the back and his hedge in the front. Ellen thought sometimes that he used the house solely as a passage-way for his shears. In Thomas's time the roses had grown wild and unpruned. But she never cut them, nor any of the flowers in her garden. In Ellen's mind, cut flowers were only for funerals and weddings, so when she saw the parade of floats of eye-dazzling colour, she tried not to think of those she had buried, for it said in the brochure that she had to enjoy herself.

The Pickering Alice, on the other hand, had little trouble

with that. The floats delighted her, embellishing the interval of her lover's absence. Her own garden at home was flowerless. Pickering had been a lawn man. The large stretch of green behind the house was uniformly cut and coloured. Not a blade was out of place, nor any green greener than another. Alice sometimes thought he loved his lawn-mower better than herself. He certainly spent more time with it. He was a cutter, was her Pickering. Between the lawn and the hedge, he mastered the art of reduction, and for the first time Alice realised how painful it must have been for him to watch Walsh's hedge grow wild.

Of the late Mr Bowers' party, only Alice Dove was undisturbed by associated recall. She was simply enjoying the parade for its own sake. The floats varied in their design; the shape of a chicken for some reason seemed to be favoured. But this theme too was varied. There were carnation chickens of bougainvillea, or hens of simple vine-leaves with black grapes for eyes and coxcombs. There were vast bottle designs too, with vintages spelt out in flowers, and as each float passed by the crowd gasped and cheered with delight and acclamation. Alice could see just the last float in the parade, that was still some distance from their stand, but she could hear the roar of approval that its sudden appearance had invited. From where she sat, she could not decipher its motif. From her viewpoint it seemed one multi-coloured blur of petal. As it approached, the crowds along the stands rose to their feet, roaring their approval. When it reached Alice's stand, it stopped, allowing for leisured examination. Its motif was very simple. It was the theme of the carnival itself. Flowers. Flowers made not of themselves, but of petals from another variety. Thus roses were fashioned from the petals of red carnations, orchids from irises and outsize chrysanthemums from the petals of the daisy. It was a float of audacious cross-breeding, an artful gesture of contempt for nature itself. The spectators applauded its skill, but as it moved away, it left a sense of disturbance in its wake, and Alice was reminded of a similar unease. On the mantelpiece of her mother's house, there was a string of ivory elephants carved out of their own tusks. They were beautiful enough until one considered their making. She had always turned away from them, disturbed.

The band brought up the rear of the parade with a drum-roll that reverberated long after the drum-sticks were laid aside. At first people thought it was a powerful echo until they saw the skies suddenly darken and felt the lash of a great and sudden rain. The angry clap of thunder underlined the unease that had trailed the last float like a dark shadow, and the wrathful rumble from the skies was an expression of deep offence at man's interference with nature, however skilful. That a rose is a rose and made only of rose, water of water, fire of fire. Divinely inimical.

There was no shelter at hand, so there seemed no point in hurrying from the stand. Yet people did, from automatic reflex, not knowing where to go. But Alice Dove did not move. She watched the tail end of the last float disintegrate in the flood that assailed it. Some children, heedless of the rain, ran towards it, stuffing their faces into its fragrance, occasionally coming up for air, their faces confetti-ed with petals.

The courier was disturbed by the turn of events. He had no contingency plans for rain. It was rare in Limassol this time of the year. He did what he could to herd his flock together and guide them behind the stand towards a café that offered some form of shelter. When they reached it, along with many others who had the same idea in mind, there was little room or comfort. So he called the bus that was waiting at the edge of the square, and marshalled his flock inside. Some gate-crashers managed to slip through his watchful eye, and he couldn't understand why the bus was so full. Now it was almost dark inside, with the rain fast and furious. 'It won't last long,' the courier said, 'but those who want can go back to the ship.' There was a chorus of approval from the passengers and, as it died away, the rain stopped as suddenly as it had begun, and the skies were bright again.

'I think I'll go back anyway,' Alice Dove said.

The courier looked at her with little surprise that trouble was coming from that quarter. Other voices dared to echo Alice's decision, amongst them, Wally, who was glad to clutch at any straw that would excuse him from the beach-stroll and the promise he had to give for romance. With his threat to leave, Mrs Dove declared her wish to stay, for much as she dreaded the beach-stroll, it was infinitely preferable alone than on the ship's deck in uncomfortable company. 'I'll stay with you,' Alice Pickering said, and Ellen needed little persuasion. If it had been practical she would never have returned to the ship again.

So they alighted from the bus into the blazing sun, the courier leading them, leaving a handful of passengers bound for the harbour. The bus swung around the square and into the city streets. Alice Dove looked about her. The waiter sat alone on the back seat. She smiled at him because she had no reason not to, and she wondered why he didn't return her smile.

When the bus reached the harbour, Alice boarded the ship and went straight to her cabin. That night she knew the ship would turn for home, and the prospect pleased her. The next few days would simply be an overture to the new life that faced her, the life she would fashion for herself out of her newly-adjusted priorities. She wanted to mark the ship's turning with some appropriate action, and she decided she might start to pack. She bent down for her suitcase and heard a knock on her door.

'Come in,' she shouted without looking.

The waiter entered. Had her back not been towards him, and a bending submissive back at that, he might have thought again. On his way to her cabin, he knew that what he had in mind was folly, that it could well spell the end of his waiting/raping career. But the challenge she presented, the anticipation of her splendid outraged struggle, drove him in her direction. He knew it was a mistake he was making, but he could not help himself, and his eyeful of her stooped unexpectant back almost unhinged his senses. I'm crazy, he said to himself, and he pounced on her like a panther. Her resistance was more splendid than he had ever hoped for, but as it turned out, too splendid for his own good.

Alice Dove was more enraged than frightened. Whatever it was that had assaulted her had interrupted the bright vision of the new life she was planning for herself, and it was this fury that fed her muscle. She lashed out, and with a strength that astonished her, to say little of what it did to him, spread-eagled as he suddenly found himself on the floor. His head lay in her suitcase, and his torso trembled with his defeat, and the fear of the terrible revenge she would wreak

184

on him. He placed a trembling hand over the tools of his trade, fearing his redundancy.

Alice looked at him. She didn't know how he'd got there, but the tingling muscle in her right arm gave her a clue. Nellie would have been proud of her. She pressed her foot on his stomach just in case there remained a shadow of doubt in his twisted mind as to who was the victor. She stared at him and wondered what to do. He wriggled a little and she dug her foot more firmly into his stomach.

'Lie still,' she hissed at him. 'I'm deciding what to do with you.'

His fear, the terror of not knowing what alternatives she had in mind, melted his trembling bowel, as if he knew his chips were down, and he was merely obeying the humiliating rules of quietus. He would have produced a throat-rattle too, if only to satisfy what he knew was her present wish, his total and degrading annihilation. He'd heard tales told of Alice's sort of woman, and castration was always their theme. He thought of his wife and their two daughters, both of them thwarted attempts at a son. He intended to try and try again for an heir, a proper heir, a serious trustee, one who could take his name and hand it down to eternity. He looked at her, pleading.

But his fears were misplaced. A month ago perhaps, Nellie-imbued, she might well have savoured his dismember-ment, seeing it as a lynching of his whole gender. Now she saw him as a pathetic little creature who was representative of nothing but human frailty. She was able now to pity him, with a pity without compassion. His terror had drained him of all strength, and Alice knew she could do with him what she willed. She dragged him along the floor by his collar and, when they reached the door, she told him to get up. 'We're going to the purser,' she said.

He tried to struggle free, but her grip was iron. She drove him along the corridor. He feared that if he offered the least resistance, she would offer in return, and pretty ungraciously, the coup-de-grâce. In the corridor he racked his mind for some story to cover himself. But since he had little time for invention, and even less equipment, he decided on a total denial of whatever accusation she chose. It was his only chance. She pushed him before her into the purser's office.

He was glad to notice that the purser was alone. Usually the office was milling with staff, but today they were probably besporting themselves in Limassol.

'What is it?' the purser said, though he suspected the reason for her call by the rage on her face and the terror in his.

'He tried to rape me,' she said. That was the simple truth of it. It required no adornment.

'She's lying,' he trembled. 'It was more like the other way round. She asked me to ... well you know what. I said no. I was furious,' he said, with righteous indignation. 'She's twisted it all round.' He'd given only a brief resumé of the whole story, he said. For her sake he'd spare the purser the more sordid details. He hoped it would do.

She slapped him across the face, which only confirmed in the purser's mind her fury at his rejection.

'D'you wish to bring charges, Madame?' he said. He had to play it by the rules of the book. If she insisted, he would try, for her own sake, to dissuade her.

Alice thought for a while. She was not hopeful of her chances of prosecution. She had already sniffed the purser's incredulity. Her Venice adventure, now known to all the ship, marked her as a woman of a certain instability. They would recall her dungarees, and see in them an expression of man manqué. There was little point in fighting a male conspiracy. She couldn't win. She didn't even want to try.

'No,' she said, 'but you ought to keep an eye on him.'

Her decision not to bring charges confirmed her guilt in the purser's mind.

'We're very grateful,' he said. 'I will, as you suggest, keep an eye on him.'

He said it for her sake, but in fact the purser had no intention of surveillance. The man had worked for the ship's company for well on fifteen years and his work and demeanour had never given cause for complaint. Occasionally there had been the odd plaintiff, the lonely woman of a certain age, who had spluttered her poor fantasies onto his desk, but he had understood. He was, after all, a man of some experience and compassion. He had always managed to calm them and to send them away with soothing words. He knew from long experience that cruising was an adventure that induced all kinds of fantasies, especially in those who were emotionally deprived. Yes, he was a man of experience alright, and a bit of a psychiatrist too. In his job you had to turn your hand to anything.

The waiter thought he'd got off very lightly indeed. But he was not one to push his luck. He had to acknowledge an end to his nocturnal flittings, at least for the duration of this cruise. He could rely on Ellen Walsh to keep her mouth shut, and the chiffoned Alice too, for reasons of her own. But this one, this dungareed one, would have no shame in bruiting her assault abroad. Ellen was often in her company, and she might be encouraged by her story to offer her own dilemma, and together they would make a formidable united front against him. No, he would have to lie low, and with all of them. The chiffoned one too. He would take no risks. He would keep out of their sight as much as possible, confining his duties to the gaming rooms which they did not frequent, and to tables in the dining-room annexe which were out of their sight. He thought of the ten ensuing nights of enforced abstinence and was overcome by a profound depression.

Alice went on deck. At the far rail, she spotted Wally Peters and made a quick turnaround to avoid him. She didn't want to be burdened by his marriage plans, which she now saw as faintly unfulfillable. Her mother had chosen to stay on the island. It might have been the first move of her withdrawal. Alice was glad of it. Wally could enrich nobody's life, least of all, poor devil, his own. She leaned over the opposite rail, and felt a strange paradoxical sense of victory. What had happened in the purser's office was a purgative experience. It had finally cleansed her of the residue of her hate. She had frightened the life out of him, and for her it had been enough. She did not wish to punish him further. She was satisfied. She smiled to herself. The ship would turn itself tonight, and head for home, and for the new life that she was prepared to risk yet again. She made her way back to her cabin. It had begun to rain, and by the time she'd left the deck, the thunder had darkened the skies. Not long afterwards, the rest of the passengers returned to the ship, the promise of beach-romance unfulfilled. During dinner, the storm abated, and a full bright moon lit the upper deck and guided the ship's turning. In their cabins, the passengers heard the rumble of

engines and knew, according to the quality of their enjoyment, that the cruise was already half over or only half
begun. Ellen listened to the engines with joy, counting the
nights of terror that she still had to serve. The Pickering Alice
trembled with the engine's reverberations, and wondered how
she could face the dawns without him. Wally Peters rehearsed
a catalogue of deceptions which, with small repetition, would
last the journey home. Mrs Dove was doing likewise, and
thinking all the time of her garden.

That night at the ship's dance to celebrate its turning, Alice
Dove put on her cerise ball gown. Her golden hair hung
loosely to her waist. To the observer's eye, she was of rare
beauty, and Alice dwelt inside that radiance with a greater
comfort and assurance than she had ever known.

CHAPTER ELEVEN

A false reprieve

At breakfast the next morning, Ellen was elated. She was almost grateful that she had been subjected to her ordeal for the intoxicating relief it offered when it was all over. For over she believed it to be. That night she had slept, and was not for one moment disturbed. It was as if the ship's turning had marked the end of the storm, its perils weathered and it was all over now bar the homecoming. She felt strangely heroic, with a need to recount her exploits, the dangers she had passed, and her stubborn survival. It was only the realisation that there was no-one to tell that blunted the edge of her elation.

Alice Pickering, on the other hand, was deeply downcast, and Ellen couldn't understand it any more than Alice could her friend's sudden well-being. For Alice, too, had seen in the ship's turning, an ending of an era of sorts, not of dangers, of dire threats, of hints of mortality, but an era of new dimension, of enlightenment and sheer passionate joy. For Alice, there was no triumph in the ship's turning, and no tale, even with an audience, to tell. Except to herself, over and over again, which she would have to do in order to preserve its credibility. Her greatest fear was that he had remained in Limassol. That day, she prowled the ship looking for him. She did not even bother to excuse herself from Ellen, or to offer any reason for her frequent absences. In her desolate state, she was past caring what other people thought, and she would have asked the other stewards where he was, and totally without shame or concealment. But she had no idea of his name, a fact which had always excited her, but which now drove her to despair.

'Where are you going?' Ellen asked for the hundredth time that day, when Alice rose from her deck-chair for yet another restless sortie.

'Mind your own,' Alice snapped at her, her nerves danger-ously stretched. Then regretted it, for Ellen had nothing to do with her melancholy. Ellen was staggered by the affront, and generously thought her friend unwell.

'I'm sorry,' Alice manged to blurt out. 'I'm just very restless today.' And she was off in her agitated way, seeking the nameless source of a bliss that, until this time, she had never in her life known. God help me, she whispered to herself, but I cannot live without him. When evening came, with no sign or smell of him, she retired to her cabin, headached, Ellen was told, with a request to be left alone to sleep it off. With little hope in her heart, she nevertheless chiffoned and powdered herself. There were tugboats out of Limassol. He might have been delayed.

Ellen on the other hand, did not begin to bother about his presence. She was convinced that he had been left in the wake of the ship's turning. 'Let's play a round of solo,' she suggested before dinner. There were four of them, a tidy number for the game. The others were grateful for the suggestion. It relieved Mrs Dove and Wally of the silences between them, of the truths untold, the candour stifled and honesty withheld. Over a game of cards they could look one another in the eye, and make their irrelevant bids. 'We're on our way home,' Mrs Dove said, opening with a pass. The delight in her voice did not please Wally who assumed that she was looking forward to the preparations for their wed-ding.

'You'll have lots to do when you get home,' Ellen said innocently. 'Getting married, moving house. You must both be very excited.'

Wally avoided Mrs Dove's eye, and Mrs Dove, his, so neither of them noticed. But Ellen did, and found it rather worrying, and Alice Dove noticed it too, and with much relief. Wally was quick to make a bid even though he could only manage a pass, but one word, feeble as it was, was enough to divert the conversation in a less threatening direction. Alice Dove and Ellen passed too, and it was up to Mrs Dove to re-deal.

'That was quite a storm yesterday,' Wally said, frantically filling the silence that could have led anywhere.

'Most unseasonal,' Ellen said and surprised herself, because that was exactly what Mr Bowers would have said, in that very language, in that very style. She felt as though he were speaking through her, and she smiled with a deep sense of privilege. She was pleased, too, that she could already recall him without sorrow. She considered that, all in all, the cruise had been a valuable experience both in living and its counterpart, and she knew that the woman who was returning to her hedge-less terraced house, was a much wiser one than she who had left it. She felt a little sorry for Alice who, throughout the cruise had either had a headache or a vacant stare. The experience could have done little for her.

She picked up her cards. It was a poor hand once again, and she comforted herself with the old saying of 'unlucky at cards, lucky in love'. I'm sixty-three years old, she thought to herself. I'm still a young woman. Mr Bowers fancied me, so there must be others. When she got home she would join a club. She decided to go to evening classes and learn a foreign language. Such ideas startled her. What a pity, she thought, that Alice was such a stick-in-the-mud.

Mrs Dove passed too, and Wally commiserated with her. 'You know what they say, don't you?' he said, and though everybody knew, he spelt it out. 'Unlucky in cards, lucky in love,' he said, and when he heard it he deeply regretted it, for such a statement was asking for trouble.

'Well in that case, I hope you pass too,' Mrs Dove said, and her daughter thought her mother had weathered that one rather sensibly.

'I'll go for an abundance,' Wally said. 'A royal one,' unaware that in his bid he had declared himself a rejected lover.

Mrs Dove looked at her daughter and raised her eyes to the ceiling. They played. It was clear that Wally had a very good hand. He grabbed each trick with greedy triumph. The play was almost exhausted and Wally had only one more trick to make so that his bid would be honoured. Then Alice trumped his ace, without spite or pre-planning. She had simply overlooked the fact that she had one trump left. Wally seethed with fury. His game was lost. He began to shout. His volume, if not his words, accused them all of cheating. Ellen tried to calm him. 'Well, you must be lucky in love,' she said, but that was the very last thing that Wally wished to be lucky in at that moment.

'It's only a game,' Mrs Dove protested, and wondered how she could have ever thought of marrying him.

He collected the cards and put them aside, signifying that he didn't want to play any more. 'I'm going for a walk,' he said petulantly. No-one tried to dissuade him. He shoved his seat back and was gone.

'You're going to have quite a handful there, Mrs Dove,' Ellen said, then regretted it for it was none of her business.

'I'll train him,' Mrs Dove said. 'He's lived alone too long.'

Alice looked at her mother warily. She couldn't imagine that she intended to go through with the marriage. But Mrs Dove did not mean to let anyone into her plans, not even her daughter. It would have been unkind to Wally to make others party to her decption. 'In time he'll make a good husband,' she added. 'He's really very kind, you know.'

Alice Dove was not happy with what she heard.

'Don't worry,' her mother said, seeing the look of concern on her face. 'Everything will be alright.'

'As long as you know what you're doing,' Alice said, and they left it at that.

They heard the first dinner-gong. A renewed appetite was part and parcel of Ellen's sense of well-being. Alice had not yet returned from her cabin, and Ellen was anxious to dine. She did not want to start without her friend so she decided to go and see if Alice had dressed for dinner.

She knocked on her cabin door. 'Come in,' she heard, in a voice of such excitement and girlish expectation that she thought she'd come to the wrong cabin. But the number checked, even if the voice did not match. She opened the door warily. 'Alice?' she called. She was in time to see the look of extreme disappointment on her friend's face, to notice the chiffon nightdress carefully pleated over the sheet – clearly no casual drape – and to sniff the powders and the perfumes that hovered like a tester over Alice's bed. Nothing in the room seemed to have anything to do with headache, either for its cure or aggravation.

'How are you Alice?' Ellen said. 'Is your headache gone?' This last, with a touch of doubt that it had ever been. 'How are you?' she said again, with emphasis in its repetition, clearly indicating that the enquiry referred to her mental health.

192

'I've got a terrible headache,' Alice insisted, and heartily wished that Ellen would go away.

'Aren't you going down to dinner?' Ellen asked.

'I'm not hungry.' Alice was glad it was dinner-time. If he was there, and serving, he could not help but notice her absence and assume that she was in her cabin. It was an opportunity for a safe visit. She wished Ellen would go and eat and, by her presence in the dining-room, declare her own absence.

'Shall I get a steward to bring you something?' Ellen asked.

Alice hesitated. It was a gamble that Ellen would pick the wrong steward. But she decided to chance it. 'That would be very kind of you,' Alice said.

'I'll do it straightaway,' Ellen obliged, glad to leave the cabin and its unfathomable odours. For the sights and smells of them were familiar. As she walked to the dining-room, Ellen recalled her second nuptials, the chiffoned nightdress, the perfumed talc that had driven Thomas into a frenzy of excitement. She couldn't understand it. There was no Thomas in Alice's life, and certainly not on this ship, and she feared that her friend was dwelling in some kind of fantasy, like a young teenager, or worse, a regressed child. She entered the dining-room and looked around for a motherly waitress, someone fat and full of comfort, and to her she gave Alice's order.

She went to the table where Wally and the Doves were already seated. Wally seemed to have recovered from his sulks, and was once again, at Mrs Dove's request, describing his fictitious London address. He had a poor memory which made him an inept liar, and the hitherto four-bedroomed house was now enlarged to five. He remembered the two bathrooms, and knew three to be fantasy-land and a proper give-away, but he entirely forgot the river and the balconies that overlooked it. Mrs Dove had to jog his memory, and it occurred to her that she knew his house better than he did, though she had never set foot in it, and now suspected that neither had he. She now had less scruple in rejecting him, even without the delicacy she had planned.

'I hope there'll be room for me if I visit,' her daughter said half jokingly.

'You'll be very welcome,' Wally said. 'You too, Ellen,' he added, thankful that he had so many bedrooms.

'You're going to have an awful lot of housework, Mrs Dove,' Ellen said.

'Oh no.' Wally decided to go the whole way. 'I have a resident housekeeper. She does the cooking and the washing goes to the laundry.' In his enthusiasm, he'd forgotten his utility room and the washers and the driers that it housed.

'Why d'you have a utility room then?' Mrs Dove goaded him.

'Oh just for small things,' Wally said, and he reddened, not from the shame of his smalls, but for the lie that had exposed him.

Alice Dove, seeing through the whole charade, now mercifully changed the subject, and asked after her namesake's health. But that was a subject Ellen didn't want to dwell on, so she dismissed it quickly, assuring them that Alice's headache would soon pass. She would say no more. The chiffon and the perfume still nagged at her.

The rest of the meal was silent, and all retired early, except for Alice Dove who took a turn about the deck and contemplated the sea. For the first time in many days she thought of Nellie, and in the same thought, of the headached Alice, the unhappy Ellen, and her hoodwinked mother. Before the cruise, their common denominator in her mind, would have been the simple fact of 'woman', woman as victim, woman as the oppressed. Now the thought of such words embarrassed her. They were, all of them, just people, and if there were any formula at all, it was that of loneliness. And Wally? Poor Wally. Lonely too, like all of them. All inconsolable. Beyond gender.

At breakfast next morning, Alice Dove noticed his absence at the serving-table, and then realised that she hadn't seen him for some days. Perhaps the purser was indeed keeping a wary eye on him, confining him perhaps to the kitchens and far from temptation. Ellen had had another undisturbed night. She had achieved a calm that she had never known, a serenity that was impervious to any disturbance. She regarded Alice's continuing headaches with concern, but she did not let them ruffle her. Alice's headaches were now very real, as it became more and more clear to her that her lover was pledged to Limassol. She still prowled the dining-room with her eyes, but with less and less confidence. She knew she would have to pull herself together, to learn to live without him, as she would have to do in any case, even if he came to her cabin before landing. You should be ashamed of yourself, Alice Brewster, she said to herself, and was startled that the name of Pickering had left her mind, unnoticed, leaving not a trace of scruple, as if it had never been there at all. She was anxious now about her homecoming, how she could adjust to the non-Pickering Alice, wedded to a past of so many married years, during which time she had hardly known herself. She must try not to be angry with Pickering. It was not his fault he did not speak her language, a tongue of which she herself was ignorant at the time. Poor Pickering, she thought. He was more in danger of her pity than her rage.

Another cause of Alice's concern was Ellen, and their future relationship. Alice had never kept a secret from Ellen, largely because her life held little to hide. But now there was a barrier between them, and of her own making. There was no way she could confide in Ellen, and she must guard against feeling superior, a woman of the world, with an experience under her belt, and elsewhere, of things Ellen had never dreamed about. Except marginally perhaps, with Thomas, but they'd been married and the legality of their contract must have detracted from its joy. She hoped her experience didn't show on her face. Ellen was a wily one, with a knack for milking information. I must keep my lips firmly sealed, she instructed herself.

At dinner that evening, Alice Dove looked for him again and her brow was puckered as she scanned the dining-room. Her namesake, who was doing exactly the same, caught her eye, and both wondered who the other was looking for.

The days passed, measured out in Alice's headaches, and Ellen's daily deliverance. Ellen was no longer afraid. Already the experience had become a nightmare of the past, which terror was diluted more and more on each rested awakening. And so confident was she in her deliverance, that, one evening at dinner, she casually said, 'I wonder what happened to our steward. I haven't seen him around for the last few days.' She heard her own voice as steady and firm, and she knew that the nightmare was truly over.

Alice Dove felt herself redden, as if accused. She had told

195

nobody about her steward or purser encounter. It had seemed to her to be a very private affair, together with its outcome. She felt no need to share it.

'I was wondering too,' the Pickering Alice said, relieved that he was mentionable at all. 'Did he come back from Limassol?' she dared.

'Yes,' Wally said. 'You remember Alice' – this to the other one – 'He was on the same bus as we were. We all boarded the boat together.'

'Yes, he's on the boat somewhere,' Alice Dove said, and suddenly her namesake uttered a little cry, and once again excused herself from the table with a sudden headache.

'You'll have to go to a doctor about those headaches of yours,' Mrs Dove said. 'They're all too frequent.' And Ellen wondered what kind of doctor would know the answer.

'Shall I come with you?' Ellen said, rising, but Alice brushed quickly past the table. Ellen was sure she saw tears in her eyes.

Poor Alice. She had been on her way to accepting her rejection on the grounds of his Cyprus connection. She would, with much pain it's true, have relinquished him to his wife and family. But to another, another like herself, no better, no more willing, no more accommodating, such a thought was insupportable. She reached her cabin and lay on the bed, sobbing like a child. By the time Ellen knocked on her door, she did indeed have such a raging headache that her mind was too fuddled for expectation. So when she saw Ellen in the doorway she was not disappointed.

'Shall I get the doctor?' Ellen said. 'And why are you crying?'

'It's the pain,' Alice said. 'I've just taken some aspirin. It'll pass.'

'I'm getting the doctor anyway,' Ellen said and she was out of the cabin before Alice could protest.

She lay there letting the pain wash over her. She was not worried about the doctor's visit. There was no way of diagnosing heart-ache, no instrument to record her shame and rejection, and, above all, no wherewithal to monitor the sudden pulse in her thighs which only now, after sixty-odd years, had found its own God-given rhythm. She wondered who her replacement was and imagined a dining-room of faces for a possible candidate. It did not occur to Alice that her suitor was in any way indisposed. Since he was now known to Alice to be on board, his absence could only be attributed to the whole days and nights he was loving another.

The doctor came shortly after Ellen's departure. Ellen was with him, hovering around the bed like a mother hen. She watched as Alice submitted herself to temperature, blood-pressure and heart-investigation. When it was all done, the doctor declared that he could find nothing wrong, but if the headaches continued, Alice should see her own doctor for blood tests.

'Not upset about anything, are you?' he said casually, as he put his instruments away.

'Oh no,' Alice protested. 'Everything is very nice here.'

'Nothing worrying you at home?'

'No,' Alice said. Except the emptiness, she thought, that awaited her on her return.

He gave Alice two tablets. 'Take these,' he said. 'You'll be right in no time.'

There was a knock at the door. Both Ellen and Alice trembled, the one in fear and the other in hope of his sudden reappearance. But it was Wally who had put his head round the door, a large hospital visitor's grin on his face, tinged with the embarrassment of being in the presence of the sick. He was delighted to find a diversion and the chance for some conversation that had nothing to do with his fictitious marital home. He was followed by Mrs Dove and Alice, and all carried behind their backs small bunches of flowers which they had picked from the dining-tables. They made much ceremony of handing them over. Alice was thankful that no-one knew her secret, or the flowers would have been a tribute to her debauchery. They sat around the cabin while Ellen assured them of Alice's recovery.

'I knew a man had headaches once,' Wally said. 'He died. You don't always recover from headaches, you know. Affects the brain.'

'Oh don't be so morbid Wally,' Mrs Dove said. 'My husband was plagued with headaches all his life, and he always recovered. He died of a heart-attack. Now that's something you don't always recover from.'

'Oh yes,' Ellen agreed. 'I know all about that. So does Alice. Don't we, Alice?'

Alice had to think very carefully before fully understanding what Ellen was referring to. Poor Pickering had gone again. 'Oh yes,' she said, after a pause in which she slowly gathered its relevance, 'Oh yes,' she said again, enthusiastically, more for her own recall than for poor Pickering's demise. 'You had two went that way, Ellen,' she added, and it sounded as if it were one of Ellen's nasty habits.

'This conversation's getting very morbid,' Alice Dove said. 'Let's change the subject.'

Then Wally felt very threatened and he got up as if to leave. 'Just came to pay my respects. It's late and the nights are getting shorter, you know. It's already one o'clock in the morning in England,' he said.

'But this isn't England,' Mrs Dove said.

'But it soon will be. Good old England,' Wally said.

'And then you'll have all the excitement of your nuptials,' Ellen said, hearing the descent once more of Mr Bowers' mantle.

Wally excused himself very quickly and stumbled out of the door, and Alice Dove wondered why her mother seemed not in the least bit perturbed. 'We must go too,' she said, and her mother rose from her seat. Ellen was the last to leave. She leaned over Alice's bed and kissed her on the forehead. She couldn't explain such an action to herself, and neither could Alice, but both were glad of it, because in some way it sealed their future companionship.

It was the last day of the cruise. They would be docking at Southampton the following morning and there was still no sign of him. A great champagne dinner and cabaret was planned for the evening, and Ellen and Alice decided to treat themselves to a hair appointment. Mrs Dove, fearful of being left alone with Wally – their non-commitment as to wedding plans was now becoming clear to both of them, and embarrassing too – decided to treat herself as well. And Alice, her daughter, who never in her life had set foot in a hairdressing salon, was eager for a new experience. They were washed, set and dried simultaneously, over four bowls, in adjacent chairs, and under neighbouring driers. It was at the drier stage that conversation began, a conversation that had to compete with the continual buzz of the drier, so that it was adequately audible to the participants but of thunderous volume to those outside the drying-hoods. And thus, unaware of audience, the four ladies took upon themselves to discuss the only living human being they knew in common. Wally.

'I don't believe he's got a five-bedroomed house in London,' Alice Dove set the ball rolling. Her statement of non-belief rang through the salon like an alarm and the other wet and already-dried clientèle cocked their ears for the cause of Alice's suspicion.

'It started off by being four bedrooms,' Mrs Dove had to admit, yelling her doubts across the hair-strewn floor.

'And what about those utilities?' Ellen screamed.

'And the en-suite.' Alice made what she thought was a timid contribution, but it was received with deafening echo.

The Doves began to giggle, and Ellen said, 'Are you really going to marry him?'

Now there was much speculation in the salon as to the identity of the groom who might not make it. The clients were silent, holding their breath for the next clue. You could have heard a hair-pin drop.

'D'you think I should?' Mrs Dove asked.

'Mrs Stella Peters,' Ellen said. 'It sounds quite nice, I think.'

Now there was a buzzing in the auditorium. The last remark was undoubtedly a vital clue, but it meant nothing to any of them. Wally was a man of brash bonhomie who would, on self-introduction, offer only his Christian name, and the shortened version at that. He was too insecure to offer his complete handle, for that might have been inviting a serious relationship and he was only capable of the short and shallow connection that his offer of a mere forename implied.

Could it be that man who was always around that drying quartet, that Wally who had made the rounds of the ship, clinging to this group and that, like a spasmodic leech? The dry clients tossed the name around, soliciting each others' opinions. They decided that it must be he and, in the same breath, that on no account must she marry him. She or anybody. And this opinion they gave without lowering their voices with the security that the rumbling driers afforded them. But at that very moment, when they were tossing his name unceremoniously off the marriage lists, Mrs Dove popped her head out of the drier for a bit of a cool-off.

'That Wally,' she heard. 'Why, I wouldn't have him near me. He's so vulgar. Like a lorry-driver.'

Mrs Dove wondered why they were talking about her never-intended, and quickly slipped her head back into place. Then she heard the difference between the silence without and the rumble within and she realised that their conversation had been overheard. She felt wretched, more on poor Wally's behalf than her own. and so she set out to defend him. 'I think I will marry him,' she shouted. 'I know he seems vulgar at times, but he has a heart of gold.' She practically screamed this last into the astonished salon, and she popped her head out once again and was satisfied with the deafening silence that greeted her.

The unhooded women were now very anxious to have their hair-sets finished. No one of them wanted to be around when Mrs Dove roared out of the drier. Her daughter was so astonished by her mother's decision, that she was silent. Deeply disappointed, too, but she knew it was none of her business. Ellen and Alice were quiet too, and for the same reasons. Mrs Dove, her face already flushed by the heat of the drier, stared out from under the hood like a fiery dragon, daring challenge from any quarter. Now there was a silence in the whole salon, both from the wet and the dry.

After a while, the quartet were released and led to adjacent chairs for the comb-out. Alice sat next to her mother. She leaned over and whispered, 'Are you really serious about Wally?'

'I don't know,' her mother said, 'but I won't be influenced by the opinion of others.'

Well, that in itself was a milestone, Alice Dove thought, from a woman who all her life had been afraid to listen to the dictates of her own heart. Who married her father because he was of the opinion that he was good for her, who stayed with him till he died because it was his version of her duty, who even mourned him, heeding his instructions from the grave which taught her where her obligations lay. And who had heeded him since, together with the neighbours who were of the opinion that her husband was a good man, that it would be ungracious to his memory to think of marrying again, that she should not plant vegetables in a garden he had devoted to flowers, though her heart yearned for them, and that she didn't need a colour television, because black and white had been good enough for the good Mr Dove, and should certainly be good enough for her. This last in a remonstrative whisper. She had listened to them all, the voice from beyond, and those from the here and now, until her ears ached. Now the worm had turned, and turned splendidly.

But in such a turning there was risk. Mrs Dove might make a rash decision out of simple defiance, and pleased as her daughter was with her mother's sudden independence, she was aware of the dangers that that entailed. She did not know what to say. Advice could be construed as opinion, and opinion, judgement, an attitude her mother had rightly rejected. Yet her silence could be interpreted as advice too. 'Whatever you do, Mother, I'm sure it will be right for you,' Alice said, and again she put her hand on her mother's arm, and Mrs Dove's original decision was again confirmed. That Wally had no place in her life, nor any man who could not value her.

The Pickering Alice looked at herself in the mirror and, despite the rollers that surrounded her face, she was pleased with what she saw. She was not having her hair done for the champagne supper. In her ever-hopeful heart, it was for him, and their last dawn together, for she had convinced herself that he would not let her leave the ship without loving her one last time.

Ellen on the other hand had regained her confidence that, for whatever reason, he had most certainly tired of her. She decided to invest in a hair-net so that the set would last her for her homecoming. For diametrically opposed reasons, the two women left the salon with joy and expectation in their hearts. One of them would have to lose, and, for either of them, it would be shattering.

The afternoon was devoted to packing, and for most of the passengers it was a pleasing occupation. The fantasy was beginning to wear thin, and all the faces seemed frighteningly similar. Ellen emptied her wardrobe but for the single evening-gown reserved for the champagne supper. Then she spent the rest of the afternoon writing tardy postcards to her children and grandchildren. As long as they were posted on the ship, she could blame the postal services for their late delivery. Before she dressed for dinner, she completed her packing, leaving some small things she might need before disembarking. She checked on each drawer. Her Venice memento still lay open on her bedside table. Though it had nothing to do with Venice, it was certainly its most salient souvenir. She folded it together and laid it on top of her clothes. She would strap down the case in the morning.

In her cabin, Alice delayed her packing. Instead, she bathed, powdered and chiffoned. She had to be prepared for his last-minute changes. Tomorrow at dawn the ship would dock at Southampton and he would have his duties to attend to. She had to be prepared for him to dawn her afternoon. She lay on the bed and waited.

In his cabin, the waiter raged with gargantuan appetite. His ten days abstinence had in no way blunted his lust. Indeed it had fed it. For the past few nights, he had wrestled with the temptation to go to work on a reluctant client. The dungareed one was out of the question. That would be pushing his luck too far. And the chiffoned one was too easy a pushover to merit his splendid lust. It had to be that other one, that one with whom his alibi was secure. Even if she had conferred with the dungareed one, there would be little point in blowing his cover at this late stage. It would be their last encounter. She would be mindful of that, and her great relief would prompt her to let it lie. He convinced himself he would be running no risk, and he lay on his bed barely able to contain his excitement.

In the passengers' quarters, the chiffoned Alice waited patiently and Ellen dressed for the ball.

At dinner Mrs Dove was very solicitous of Wally and hung onto his arm with the public gesture of possession. After the Wally-discussion she had overheard in the salon, she felt obliged to protect him. Wally, on his part, was unnerved by her possessiveness, and since this was the last night of cruising, he felt threatened by commitment. But though she held his arm firmly, she said nothing to him, nothing about future plans, or even a request for his address. She smiled at him, and he at her. Neither would commit further.

The Pickering Alice had eventually de-chiffoned herself.

But she was still not entirely without hope. There was one more dawn to go. And, to fill in the time, she ate her supper daintily, sipped her champagne, and longed to change into chiffon. Ellen looked at her and saw that old blissful gaze. Something had happened to Alice during the cruise. Something had changed her, Ellen thought. And Alice thought the same of Ellen, without knowing the cause. And both at that moment realised that they each held a secret and that no garden-wall encounter would ever reveal it.

What the cruise-brochure had described as a cabaret was simply the band and the singer who had performed at the fancy-dress ball. When dinner was over, there was dancing and all of the late Mr Bowers' party would have wished to retire. Except for Alice Dove, who was dancing with one of tthe crew. Ellen and Alice had no reason to stay in the ballroom but for the pleading look on Mrs Dove's face, imploring them not to leave her alone. For some reason, which neither Ellen nor Alice could understand, Wally's face wore a similar look. So they sat around, wondering why Wally didn't lead his intended onto the floor.

'Well I'll be glad to get home,' Ellen said, for the sake of something to break the silence.

But home was dangerous territory for Wally, and fictitious too. He was weary of the fiction, especially since he could not remember the details.

'Yes, I think three weeks of a cruise is enough,' Mrs Dove said, skirting the issue that she feared as much as Wally.

'But you two will have a lot to do,' Alice said.

'Oh yes,' Wally agreed gamely. 'We will, won't we?' He turned a smile on Mrs Dove. He still didn't know her name. If he ever told the story of his breach of promise, he would invent a name for her. She reminded him of a Bertha, a woman of that name and similar appearance who had rejected him some time ago. He would christen this one Elizabeth, a name which in his ear rang with beauty and romance. 'Shall we dance?' he said, seeing that as the only way to avoid the repetitive subject of conversation which those two busy-body women were so intent on pursuing. He guided Mrs Dove onto the floor, and Ellen and Alice felt free to retire. As they were parting on the upper deck, Alice said,

'Shall we have supper together tomorrow night? I'll make a little roast.'

'I'll bring the wine,' Ellen said, smiling. They parted content. It seemed to both of them that a new pattern of future living had established between them. Each, unknown to the other, had a secret to conceal, a state of mind which promised a less humdrum relationship than one in which everything about the other was known and unchangeable.

Alice went straight to her cabin, chiffoned, powdered, and waited. Ellen opened her door and was surprised that she had forgotten to switch off her light. She regretted her lack of thrift, and partially to atone for that, she slipped her hand through the door and switched the light off. Through the crack in the door, she could see the eight-starred glint of her Venice souvenir. It was the only illumination. It was not until she was inside her cabin, and her door closed, that she allowed herself the treat of illumination. But what it illumined, horrified her. He was sitting on the bed, awaiting her return. She gave a little cry. There was a terrible menace in his eye. The thought crossed her mind to escape. She could return to the ballroom. But, sooner or later, she would have to retire, and he looked as if he could most certainly out-wait her, both with patience and fury. She consoled herself with the thought that this had to be the last time.

'Let's get on with it,' he said. His voice was shaky and it pointed to a frailty in other parts of him, and with this thought, Ellen panicked, for if he failed to perform, it was she he would punish, and she prayed for his swift and triumphant function, so that it could be well over and done with. She moved towards the bed, aware of her chilling self-detachment. She watched herself lie down to accomodate him. His face, above hers, had an eerie quality, that of a nightmare that turned out not to be a dream after all. He went about his business straightway, mechanically she thought, reciting his filth like a parrot by rote. It seemed to Ellen, for the first time, that this performance of his was something he had to do, from some driving inner force that had nothing to do with pleasure or appetite. She looked at her watch. It was ten-thirty. By eleven, at the latest, she should be free of him, free to sleep, with no more nightmares to fear. She lay back, trying to relax, and let him get on with

204

it. She closed her eyes and could have slept while he was at work, so sublime was her indifference. But something worried her. It was his recital in her ear. It lacked its usual appetite, its salivation, its hiss. It was arid, tired, and given now to such repetition that it was meaningless. She looked again at her watch and was uneasy to notice that over half an hour had passed. She clenched her teeth and prayed for his speedy fulfillment.

He paused for a while, pressing his body on hers. She felt the weight of him and it weighed of despair. She was faintly sorry for him. He started up again, with the same monotonous recitation. He persevered this time, and was able to operate until eleven-fifteen. But still without any achievement. He took another rest, then made another attempt, and this time he sang without words. After twenty minutes, it had led nowhere. Ellen began to tremble. The fear of punishment was suddenly very real. She wished she knew how to help him. After another rest, he started yet again, with diligence, as if his whole life were at stake. Which, in his terms, it most certainly was. He went on and on until midnight. And still he would not give up. And still he achieved nothing. In a desperate effort, he made a last stand, and an unreliable one at that and it was not until twelve-thirty that he managed to resolve his exertions, as predictably as the night that must follow day. Yet despite his heavy toil, and the pathetically small pay-off, it was, at least, a result of sorts, and for that alone he was satisfied, though he hated her for having witnessed his struggle. Had he had the strength, he would have injured her, but he could barely walk of the cabin. On his way out, he caught sight of the knife lying on top of her suitcase, and with what was left of his strength, he threw it in her face. Then he shut the door after him, leaning on it for a while, and breathing heavily. He took a few slow steps, talking himself into some kind of achievement. He was like any good old war-horse, who'd taken a tumble but had risen to ride again. He didn't need any further proof that night. The chiffoned one, in any case, was too easy. She would prove nothing. So as it turned out, both Ellen and Alice were the losers, though Alice, unawares, lay powdered in her cabin.

Ellen dragged herself off the bed. She was too enraged to feel her pain. She caught sight of her face in the mirror, and knew that, in the morning, her eye would be blue. She opened her suitcase and rummaged for a handkerchief to mop up the trickle of blood that dribbled from her cheek, and in doing so, she saw a clutch of ship's notepaper she had taken from the writing-room. And then she knew what she had to do. For herself, it would offer no relief, except the satisfaction that he would lose his job, and thus she would spare countless future passengers of his torment.

She would write to the purser. That's what she would do. But anonymously, so that there could be no follow-up. She would tell him the whole truth, the complete story, as she had told it to Mr Bowers. In the light of all the facts, she would explain why she had not reported it before, and in that same light her anonymity would be excused. What pleased Ellen most was the thought of saving others from the terror of her nights, and she even managed a smile like a crusading angel.

Dear Mr Purser, she wrote, not knowing his name, and glad to extend the anonymity to her addressee. *I have had the most terrible experience on this cruise and I have decided to write and tell you all about it. There is a waiter on this ship,* she paused, realising that she did not know his name. She spent the next paragraph dealing out cards of identity, his brilliantine, his service tables, though these, she admitted, were subject to change. She realised that she was offering very little to the purser that would help him identify her attacker. She racked her memory to describe the details of his face. But she could remember no specifics. Only an ensemble, and that image was so entangled with her own rage and indignation, that it was indescribable. She remembered that he had worn point-ed patent leather shoes, but that was possibly the uniform of all stewards. Only about one thing was she certain. His smell, his brilliantine smell, and this detail she laboured, repeating it over and over again, greasing her writing with her slippery proof. She wrote about their first encounter, and the black-mailing photograph which explained her reluctance to report him. She avoided the more sordid details of their contact. Her language was polite, and her style, suburban, but when she read the letter over, she was horrified at its depravity. And at the same time, she prided herself in having survived the ordeal. She read it twice over to make sure that there were no

206

salient omissions, then she sealed the envelope and addressed it TO THE PURSER in capital letters.

She looked at her watch. It was 1.30. Overhead, she could hear faint music from the ballroom. The coast in the sleeping quarters would be clear. She put on her dressing-gown, and made her slow way down the corridor.

But he had seen her. On leaving her cabin, he had paused to rest his exhausted self on the attendants' stool at the other end of the corridor. She had not seen him, being too intent on her mission to look for impediments. He watched her as she mounted the steps that led to the administrative quarters of the ship. He saw the large envelope in her hand. He knew the evidence inside was damning. He should never have thrown that knife at her. He got up wearily and followed her at a distance.

As he expected, she stopped at the purser's office. He knew that it was closed, but she did not even try the door-handle. She seemed satisfied to slip the envelope under the door. He waited, peeping from his hide-out, and saw the triumphant smile on her face as she turned. He watched her down the corridor, and into the turn to the cabin quarters. Then, as quickly as he could, he rushed to his own.

He took a metal coat-hanger from his wardrobe, and on his way to the purser's office, he untwined it into the shape of a semi-circle. When he reached the purser's door, he slipped it underneath, and netted the envelope neatly within its arc. Carefully he withdrew his trap, and pocketed the evidence with deep satisfaction. He was not curious as to its contents. They were entirely predictable. He would read them at his leisure. Meanwhile he had to get some sleep.

In the ballroom, Alice Dove was still dancing, last-waltzing with one of the crew. Wally Peters, in his cabin, and Mrs Dove in hers, were both fast asleep, dreaming of the separate establishments that they would never leave or share. Down the corridor, Alice Pickering fingered the pleats of her chiffon, and waited for dawn.

CHAPTER TWELVE

Neighbours once more

On the morning of debarkation, Alice Pickering overslept. She had waited so long for her dawn suitor that finally she had succumbed to her fatigue and disappointment and slept till the second breakfast serving. So when she arrived in the dining-room, Ellen's black eye had already made its debut to a total lack of comment from the other guests. Perhaps they were being polite, for Ellen really looked quite dreadful. When Alice reached the table, she looked at Ellen and caught her breath.

'What happened?' she said.

'I bumped into a post last night on my way to the cabin,' she said.

'Drunk again,' Wally laughed, and the Doves thought him crude and unfeeling.

'It must be very painful,' Alice said, and she put her arm on Ellen's shoulder.

Ellen smiled, and the others noticed the glow on her face that was strangely at odds with the bruising, a serenity in the half-closed eye, as if she had received her wound with honour. She was wearing her scar with pride.

In truth, her smile was one of total confidence, for she was sure that there would be no sign of him. He would surely have been drawn and quartered by sunrise. So she was, to say the least, faintly astonished to catch sight of him in the dining-room, happily serving the late breakfast as if nothing in his life was in jeopardy. She hurriedly excused herself, protesting that she needed something from her cabin. She rushed to the purser's office and was mightily relieved to find it still closed. She returned to the dining-room and watched his smiling face with a grain of pity. He would not be smiling for long.

The ship was docking and the passengers assembled on the deck. It was farewell time. Ellen and Alice and the Doves exchanged addresses with mutual and sincere invitations to Ilfracombe and London. The stewards were portering the luggage onto the deck, and there was a rush to claim baggage. The two Alices and Ellen were separated from Mrs Dove, and they looked around to locate her and soon spotted her, standing alone, stranded with Wally in an embarrassed leave-taking. The two of them faced each other, saddled with their mutual betrothal and with nothing else to do but to say goodbye or to get married. Both of them wished to avoid the finality of such a choice. It was Mrs Dove who was the first to temporise.

'We must keep in touch, Wally,' she said.

'Oh yes,' Wally's agreement was over-hearty. 'We must definitely keep in touch.'

Neither offered their own address or asked for the other's. Both were aware of the impossibility of further communication, but they hid their awareness with smiles. Wally was certain that she was waiting for his London address, and felt that he ought to say something.

'I'll write,' he said lamely.

'That'll be very nice.' Mrs Dove smiled, and she looked around for her daughter. It did not occur to Wally that Mrs Dove was playing exactly the same game as himself. He felt himself securely off the hook, and as she took her leave, he held her arm, and, safe in the knowledge that he would never have to see her again, he generously offered her a last crumb from what he imagined would be his multi-populated table.

'I love you, honeybunch,' he said. Then he fled, threading his way through the other passengers, placing himself on the very back of the line, happy to be the last one to leave the ship.

Alice and Ellen made their way to the top of the gangway. Alice hesitated. She was loath to leave, for it meant the total abandonment of her hopes. She looked back at the ship's rail, hoping perhaps that he was watching her, his face wreathed in grief at their parting. But he was nowhere to be seen. Ellen looked around too, and seeing no sign of him, she smiled. The purser's office must have opened. She tugged at Alice's arm. Now she was as eager to leave the ship as Alice was disposed to stay. There were other passengers pushing from behind, and Alice then had no alternative but to put behind her, once and for all, the source of all her joy.

'Won't you be pleased to be home?' Ellen said.

And Alice nodded, half meaning it, for home meant safety, an anchorage, that would cushion the loss to which she must grow accustomed.

They passed quickly through customs, and as they settled into the London train, Alice was conscious of a sense of relief. She was grateful now that for the last ten days he had not come to her, for it had, in retrospect, given her time to adjust. The location of her own home would ease that adjustment, and perhaps in time, she would learn to forget him. In her heart, at least. Her body was a very different problem. For however her heart was coping, she knew that her body would forever pine for the startled joy it had once so briefly known.

'Did you enjoy it?' Ellen said, and Alice, dwelling on her amorous dawns, thought for one moment that Ellen was mind-reading. She started.

'Oh yes,' she stammered. 'The cruise was very nice. I liked the food and the company and the games, and Venice especially.' Breathlessly she reeled off all the peripherals, skirting around the core of her greatest pleasure.

'Would you go again?' Ellen said.

And for the first time, Alice realised that they need not be parted for ever. 'Oh yes,' she said quickly. 'I'd love to see Venice again.'

'You mean you'd go on exactly the same ship?' Ellen said, though for her part the idea was preposterous.

'Of course,' Alice said, for for her there was no other. 'And we don't have to wait until next year,' she said, full of excitement. 'We could go in the spring.' She thought she might buy herself a new chiffon negligée.

'I wouldn't want another cruise,' Ellen said. 'Anywhere.' Her nameless attacker was probably one of a kind, and, scattered across the high seas, they were legion. 'I think I'll stick to dry land for my next holiday,' she said.

Alice was deeply disappointed, but she said nothing. She couldn't possibly go on holiday without Ellen, and she thought Ellen was a bit of a spoil-sport. But she would not bear grudges. Ellen's eye looked extremely ungainly.

They said little more to each other during the journey, and when the train pulled into Waterloo station, they saw a group of travellers assembled on the platform under the banner of *Walton Cruises*, that very organisation with which they themselves had travelled. Alice looked at them with gnawing envy. Ellen stood still, smiling. There were many more women than men in the group, and amongst them one who stood aside, alone, and with clearly ambivalent feelings about the adventure which lay in her store. She was about Ellen's age, and from the distance, Ellen saw her as a soul sister. *I've saved you,* she whispered to herself with evangelical zeal. *And I've saved you, and you, and you,* she said, picking out the women of the group. She felt herself as their guardian angel, and for a moment she almost welcomed the experience that had, in the end, practically canonised her.

They took a taxi as their last fling of extravagance, and in the back seat they linked arms, glad to be on their way home. They parted at Ellen's gate.

'Look,' she said suddenly, pointing to the earth where once their common hedge had bloomed.

Alice peered into the ground. Despite its poisoning, the beginnings of a new hedge had stubbornly forced their way into the sunlight. On Alice's side too, it had sprouted a little, with proud green leaves, silent and still, as if offended by the mean trick they had pulled on it.

'I'm glad,' Ellen said. 'It will grow again. But this time, we'll trim it ourselves.'

A few days later, on a Sunday, Ellen and Alice went to visit their hedge-cutters. Ellen picked what was left of the roses in her garden. Walsh had planted them after all. He was entitled to savour the fruits of his toil. For Thomas she picked marguerites that had been planted years ago by another and unknown hand, and had flowered faithfully every year. Alice carried no flowers, just a small pair of shears to trim the grass where Pickering lay. He had always been fastidious about a lawn's symmetry.

Arm-in-arm, they passed through the cemetery gates to the section where their men lay. Walsh and Pickering were neighbours in death as they had been in life. Thomas lay in another section altogether and Ellen had to cross over two paths to reach him. She was glad of the distance between them. She had certain things to say to Walsh that Thomas should not hear, and even more certain things to say to Thomas. She laid the roses at Walsh's head, and then went straight to Thomas with the marguerites. This was her usual procedure. She did not want to eavesdrop on the Pickering encounter, any more than she would have wished Alice to overhear her heart-pourings to Walsh. By the time she returned from Thomas, Alice would have trimmed Pickering's lawn, and said all she had to say, and then she, Ellen, would have the territory all to herself.

'I'll be back,' Ellen said, and left Alice alone with her shears.

Alice knelt down by the side of the grave and started clipping. Normally she would talk to Pickering as she clipped away, giving him all the news of the neighbourhood, and weeping how much she missed him. But, this time, she could think of nothing to say, and she made much fuss and much noise with her shearing to cover her guilty silence. Then after a while, the need to say something, to declare at least her presence, was imperative. She put the shears down.

'Arthur,' she whispered. 'It's Alice. I miss you so much.' She wanted to say that first of all, so that whatever was to follow could be heard in the light of that loving declaration. 'I've been on a cruise,' she said. 'Me and Ellen. We went to Bordeaux, Venice and Limassol.' She paused and hurriedly took to her shears once more. 'I miss you,' she said again. He had to understand that. Then she put the clippers down. 'Arthur,' she said, 'it's over now. It's all finished. But ... well, Arthur, somebody made me very happy.' She didn't tell him who, and she most certainly didn't tell him how, but her simple declaration was confession enough and she felt much relieved when it was over. Then she was able to give him the little bits of accumulated three weeks' street gossip, punctuating each snippet of information with the assertion that he was deeply missed. Out of the corner of her eye, she saw Ellen, waiting to one side, and she wondered why Ellen had spent so little time with Thomas. Perhaps, she thought, she really didn't miss him very much and her Thomas visits had become simply formalities.

But the truth was otherwise. Ellen had no sooner laid the

213

marguerites at Thomas's head than, out of nowhere, she sniffed his brilliantine. Her hand trembled on the earth that covered him, and she was overcome by such a feeling of disgust that she had to turn away. 'It's not your fault, Thomas,' she managed to say before leaving him, but it was hard to find pleasure in his memory any more. She was desperate to get back to Walsh.

So it was with some impatience that she hovered on the edge of Alice's confidences, waiting for her to get them over with and be gone. She wondered what Alice was saying. She's probably telling him about all those headaches of hers, she thought. As if Pickering wanted to hear about that sort of thing. Alice was a terrible chatterer, Ellen thought. She coughed politely.

Alice put her shears away and smoothed her hand along the square of lawn. 'I miss you Arthur,' she said again. 'I'll see you next Sunday.' She looked up and nodded to Ellen as a sign that the coast would be clear, and slowly she rose from her knees and moved away.

It was her custom at this time to while away the Ellen/ Walsh encounter with a stroll around the graves and a reading of the headstones. And during her walk she would envy Ellen for her two visits, and wish that she, too, could make a double call. But this time, she felt no envy, and she whiled away the waiting in his recall, in the re-living of her glorious dawns. He had no grave for flowers, but at least, and at most, he was a memory.

Ellen knelt down by Walsh's side, and wept. 'I miss you so much, Walsh,' she said. 'I went on a cruise with Alice, and I didn't enjoy it very much.' She didn't tell him why. Such tales, even to the dead, were untellable. 'I miss you a lot,' she said again, and then realised how much indeed she missed him. And had begun to love him once more. She had often thought him cold, ungiving, passionless to the point of hardly touching her. Now in the wake of her nightmare experience, his coldness could be termed almost gentle. She wiped the tears away. She turned to Pickering's grave alongside. 'I even miss you too, a little bit,' she said. Then she smoothed Walsh's covering with her hand, and rose from her knees to join Alice. She wondered why her friend was smiling, and why, on catching sight of Ellen, the smile had quickly disappeared. Alice could be very strange sometimes, Ellen thought. They walked home arm-in-arm, talking of the Pickering and Walsh times, and their memories lightened both their hearts and drew them closer together.

Over the next few months, despite the winter frosts, the hedge grew with tenacious purpose, and each morning Ellen and Alice looked out of their netted windows and marvelled at the growth. At night Alice wore her chiffon and gave herself up to the pleasures that clothed her. But the cause of that pleasure was gradually clouded, and became as nebulous as the chiffon that was once its routine. Now only the pleasure itself remained. One remembers only that which one can afford to accommodate, and by that same token, Ellen's nights were full of sleep. In her dreams she saw herself as saviour. She thrilled with the zeal of salvation, and, on waking, the aura of deliverance still clung to her. But whom she had saved, and from what terrible fate, she could no longer, with any accuracy, define.

The following summer, they took their holidays at a boarding-house in Bournemouth, where Mrs Dove and her daughter were very happy to join them. Wally Peters was in a Butlin's camp in the north of England, giving a hopeful holiday-maker one of her chances, while on the blue Mediterranean, between Bordeaux and Venice, or between Venice and Limassol, according to the time and the season, a nameless waiter was plying his loveless trade.